# UNRAVELLING

*Letting Go, Getting Well.*

# UNRAVELLING
## *Letting Go, Getting Well.*

by

**Philip M. Greenfield**

Published by True Alignment.


ISBN 978-0-9561375-1-7

www.true-alignment.com


Designed by able
able-design.co.uk

Printed by
Printondemand-worldwide.com

This book is dedicated
to the be-ing
lying in weight
for every human.

# CONTENTS

# Unravelling

It has no name, no face,
And never leaves a forwarding address.

It works tirelessly, centrifugally,
Within this biology,
To preserve the form that presents
From the mirror each and every morning.

Its gentle ministrations
Are alive in me and in others.
In flowers and families,
In herds, both animal and human,
In societies and cultures.
In the restless swell of the oceans
And the drift of the tectonic plates
that mantle this glorious Earth.

It radiates from the heart of every star, and every being.

It is omnipotent, omnipresent,
And asks for no acknowledgement,
obedience or reward.


Unravelling just IS
And without it
We can never be.

# FOREWORD

I've often wondered why it is that we arrive in this world without a little Human Instruction Manual attached to some convenient aspect of our anatomy. Even the humble bottle of Tipp-ex that sits on the desk in front of me, on this grey and less than Spring-like May morning, has some handy advice printed upon it...

> • *Shake well before use* ... it says.

It even has a little bullet point before the instruction to draw my attention. Nice touch.

What else...
> • *Irritant*
> • *Dangerous for the environment*

Now why couldn't *I* have had such useful information appended to *me* when I was deposited upon this planet. If this had been the case, at least someone would have had the opportunity to alert me to the danger that I may pose to myself and others, as my life unfolded in all of its wayward glory. But no. It seems that I have to work it all out myself. 'Trial end error' it's called. And when everything goes a bit bottom-up? "Ah well..." they say. "*You live and learn...*"

Charming...

I love my MacBook. One of the reasons I decide to write this book was so that I could spend more time with it. But can you imagine this scenario at the Apple shop?

> "*There we go Mr Greenfield. Your brand spanking new and very shiny laptop computer. That'll be eight hundred of your English pounds if you please.*"

Thanks Mr Apple-shop-person. How do I make it work...?

---

*"Oh, er... well I dunno really. Just take a stab at it. Try a few things. Press a few knobs. I'm sure you'll work it out."*

OK...thanks... (wanders off)

So, in the absence of any Order of Service for this particular lifetime, and with no National Helpline to call, my curiosity has inevitably and inexorably been drawn toward the task of figuring out just how this 'human being' thing that I somehow got landed with, actually works.

I feel very fortunate to have been born into a time and a country where curiosity and expression are allowed to run free, and into a life where a measure of good fortune has seen fit to bestow upon me a handful of wise teachers, many fascinating books, and the laboratory of a bodywork therapy practice to aid me in the investigation of this worthy mystery. As the years have gone by I've frequently promised myself that at some point I'd like to have a go at writing that little *Human Instruction Manual* that was, sadly, missing from the box on arrival. I'm very pleased to announce that finally, I got round to it.

---

This book is about freedom. Actually, it's about the one and only reliable freedom that is available to us. Because we *cannot* predict the events that life will toss into our path, the only choice that we are realistically able to exercise is *how we will respond* to those events - and how many of us find that we don't seem to have much control even over that? Development of this skill - our *response-ability* - is a 'work in progress' for each individual over the course of their lifetime. Our degree of success or otherwise in this matter is determined primarily, I believe, by our proficiency in *self-awareness*: the level of refined attention that we are able to bring to our physical body, our emotional responses, and toward the processes that occur within our minds.

This book is about the breath. Our breathing is the most fundamental of all of the mechanical and physiological processes that occur in the body. Our breath is continuous from our first gasp to the final rattle, and is the very first mechanism to become *disordered* in the face of life's difficulties. Detriment to the deep, full and continuous expression of the breath, whether it be through stress, trauma, or unconscious habit, marks the start of a long and uncomfortable spiral toward poor health and unhappiness.

Actually... (come a little closer now, and for Heaven's sake keep this to yourself won't you). Just between you and me, what this book is really about is secrets and lies. It's about the power inherent in the secrets that we keep from each other and the lies that we tell, to radically alter both the structure and the internal workings of our bodies very much for the worse. It describes how the habit of withholding 'charged' information, and keeping this information hidden from significant others in our lives, has the ability to seriously damage our health, and ultimately limit the potential and length of our lives, and the lives of our children, family and friends. This sounds like a big statement. It IS a big statement. It points toward a BIG problem - an issue of great importance. More later...

It is important for me to state that this book is, at best, moderately speculative. It is based upon my personal observations of a wide variety of human biological suits, and the relationships that they have developed over time both with their owners, and with the world around them. My bodywork musings are supplemented by thirty years of martial arts practice, and forty eight years worth of intermittently bumpy life on this remarkable rock. Much of the material that you will find within this book undoubtedly lies uninvestigated within the arena of academic science, but I hope that it may stimulate some thought and discussion amongst those of you who have signed up to take a human body into your care for the foreseeable future.

Although I have, throughout these pages, wandered into the realms of philosophy and psychology, this is primarily a book about the mechanical body, a subject in which I have accumulated a moderate amount of experience and expertise over the years. Before I started writing this book, I joyfully gave myself express permission to play fast and loose with the time-honoured rules of language, spelling, grammar, punctuation, and probably many other literary doo-dahs which I would neither recognise or could possibly name. If you are one of those who has slogged tirelessly through endless years of arduous academic training to refine your skills within these fields in the pursuit of linguistic purity for the good of all mankind - please accept my deepest apologies and greatest respect.

In the acknowledgement that there really is nothing new under the sun, I thank all of the fine teachers that have enlightened and enlivened my path through life, and I sincerely hope that this little book goes some way toward a continuation of the flow of the wisdom that has been, and continues to be so freely given.

Phil Greenfield
May 2009

---

UNRAVELLING

# INTRODUCTION

To say exactly what *Unravelling* is... well, that may be a wee bit tricky, and I suspect, not really possible at this stage of human evolution. It's true that many have tried, and over the centuries *Unravelling* has been the contentious subject of much animated debate in both the halls of science, and the temples of religion. But if both of these camps were to be brutally honest, the jury is probably still out. Whatever it actually turns out to be, *Unravelling* would probably (for now at any rate) best be placed respectfully in that big red box file marked...

> 'Mysterious and Unknowable Forces Deserving Of
> Mythological Status, (And More Than A Little Reverence)'.

The effects of *Unravelling*, however... now that's a whole different matter. The effects of *Unravelling* are there for all to see, all of the time, and everywhere. Things grow. Things flourish. Things seem to hang together in a suspiciously orderly way, which may appear curiously contrary to the chaos that one might expect if this Universe in which we currently find ourselves were completely random in its dealings.

Just like its ethereal cousins, gravity and electricity, *Unravelling* is most easily recognised, defined and discussed by way of the effects that it brings to bear upon beings and things, and the activities that it gets itself involved in - literally, how it spends its days. *Unravelling* is definitely pro-life, and a great fan of evolution. It is responsible for waking the wintered seeds in order to to propel new green shoots into the warming airs of spring, and its impeccable timing nudges the gooey buds on the branches of trees, prompting them to unleash their leafy packets. It reminds those same trees to let fall their spent solar panels when the mellow heat of late summer begins to wane. *Unravelling* is the power behind the engine that heaves round the wheel of the seasons. *Unravelling* is an *urge*. An urge that is endowed with great intelligence.

Although a champion of life in all of its diversity, *Unravelling* acts from a place of seeing clearly the bigger picture, and acknowledges with unwavering certainty that the allowance of the death of certain things in order to offer birth to other things, is the only way that larger systems not only thrive, but also evolve and develop. Its accurate, but seemingly dispassionate ministrations ensure that any complex system, and the things and beings that populate that system always remain suited to the inevitable changes in their immediate environment.

So, the term Unravelling, as I am going to be using it, gives a name to that invisible but purposeful impulse in nature which silently but surely attends to bringing about the most harmonious and organised state within any biological system in relation to its surroundings, and which seeks to preserve the integrity of that system for as long as is necessary.

And what part does Unravelling play in a human life? Unravelling is always attempting to provide us with conditions that will make us more well - more 'healthy' - and is constantly and consistently acting in our highest interest. But don't be fooled. In promoting wellness, Unravelling is also the author of those illnesses that stop us in our tracks from time to time, in order that we may reflect on the state of play. Unravelling is unflinchingly directing us toward becoming the very best and most evolved beings that we can be - not just for our own individual benefit, but also for the good of those others and things with whom we share this bounded sphere (and who knows - maybe even beyond that).

We are surrounded by a restless and ever-changing environment, both globally and locally. Our individual internal systems are constantly called to respond to those changes, thus maintaining a dynamic status quo. In biology-speak, this process is called homeostasis. For example: we go for a winter walk in minus ten conditions, and our internal temperature stays at thirty seven degrees. Amazing! Similar processes are occurring throughout the multitude of machinations that go to make up our living, breathing bodies. The purpose of these processes is to preserve the integrity and (ultimately), the survival of the organism within which we reside. Unravelling is the name that I have given to the motivating push behind this endeavour.

Unravelling is the caretaker of all things that have edges to maintain and contents to retain, and is, I believe, at work not only in human bodies, but in any organised system. This urge is as evident in a galaxy as it is in a goldfish. However, having spent the last seventeen years steeped in the field of human bodywork, and not having much knowledge of either astronomy or freshwater biology, the flashlight of my curiosity naturally alights on how this unstoppable drive pertains to the subject of human well-being.

That the human biological system has a self-healing capacity is indisputable. A cut mends itself. That's it. Full stop. QED. I assume that these processes of marshalling and repair are occurring in less visible ways throughout the whole body, all of the time, and that this is reflective of a systemic impetus toward <u>order</u> and self-regulation within our physiology - in other words, an innate push toward staying 'well'. This is evidence of *Unravelling* at work. Scientific endeavour has revealed much with regard to the biochemistry of such miraculous physiological processing, but has offered little to reliably inform us regarding the nature of the *impulse* behind such commonplace wonders.

As there are many ways that we could wilfully or unwittingly delay the healing of a cut to the skin (for example, picking the wound or failing to keep it adequately clean) there must be many thousands of ways that we can (wilfully or unwittingly) stand in the way of *Unravelling* - that silent and ever-present process of self-organisation which is constantly at work within our 'human system'.

It is said that no man (or anything else for that matter) is an island. We exist in a restless ocean of interdependence which involves many individually coherent systems - atoms, cells, bacteria, plants, animals, humans, communities, nations - all partaking in the constant dance of relationship. These forms are constantly coming into being, exchanging information, and dying away. Whilst in existence, each discrete system has its edges - its own 'skin' as it were. The response of that which is 'within' the skin to conditions 'outside' is crucial to the 'health' of the organism.

We can see in the response to a cut, the intelligence of *Unravelling* at work. Seal off the perimeter! Similarly, the body's immune response to infection is a biochemical process driven by the *Unravelling* imperative, dealing effectively with what was 'out there' which has found its way 'in here' and which is not conducive to maintaining the stability of the system. In digestion, the assimilation of useful nutrients within the digestive tract, and the letting go of all that is unhelpful is a perfect example of an intelligent response. Furthermore, what is useful at any one time may change dependent on the needs of the system, and previously unwelcome information/ nutrition may start to be absorbed and included as part of the evolution of the organism into a higher, or more adapted form.

The ability of any system to throw out 'the invader' (when necessary) is fundamental to its well-being, and is driven by the invisible force of *Unravelling*. In an act of centrifugal dynamism, the streaming vitality of the organism urges from the core outwards, pushing out infection, toxicity, and other types of disturbance on gross, and also more subtle levels. This wave of cleansing may meet resistance in the medium through which it travels, producing symptoms on the levels of body, emotion and mind. In this book, I will suggest that (notwithstanding a medical emergency) it is the **allowance** of these symptoms, by way of a gentle and non-judgemental sensory awareness toward their presence, that is at the heart of making *Unravelling* an increasingly **conscious** aspect of our lives, and is one of the primary tools that we have to promote wellness, not only within ourselves, but for those around us and the world in which we reside.

**In essence, this book contains nothing new. It merely points toward principles that have been in operation since the dawn of time. *Unravelling* IS, and its processes are and always have been trundling along, whether we like the idea or not. The dilemma that we face is this: are we going to *consciously* align ourselves, by way of our free will, with this deeply intelligent and powerful river? Or will we squander our life's energy by attempting to swim against the current.**

In the light of this, I have divided this book into two sections, entitled *Aids to Unravelling,* and *Obstacles to Unravelling.* Each section contains a potpourri of topics and simple exercises which come together to create a window into the magical world of *Unravelling* - the Way of Nature.

So then. Let go and get well? Hang on and burn up? A simple choice, but a choice that needs to be consciously made within every moment of our lives until we have got the hang of bobbing along. So let's begin our journey by having a look at what we might be.

## MAPPING THE HUMAN SYSTEM

How can we describe what we are? Big job. Best make a map. Maps never accurately represent reality, but are useful for navigating the territory.

I go for simplicity every time. I've always been a great fan of maps the like of which may have been found inside the covers of great books by Tolkein and C.S.Lewis. You know the kind - Ocean, Spooky Forest, Big Mountain, 'Here Be Dragons' - that sort of thing.

So how about a threefold division? Body, Mind, Emotion. We'll add to that the notion of The Impartial Observer. Four 'bits'.

## Body

This is the word I'll use for all of the structural stuff that I notice about myself. Bone, muscle, nerves, organs, and everything else within the bounds of my skin. I notice this stuff primarily through my perception of sensation. It feels sometimes achy, sometimes heavy, sometimes light and buzzy, the sensations fleeting and ever-changing. On occasions, the sensations may become more intense, even painful, and stay awhile. Body is the 'stuff'' that I haul around day to day. I see it in the mirror. It comes to meet me when I stub my toe on the leg of the bed in the morning (again).

## Mind

This word I will use to describe mental processes. Inner monologue and dialogue which I can hear as if listening to another person. Images of past events and future fantasy. I observe these thought-images as if viewing a play, sometimes becoming lost in thought, and it seeming as if I'm actually *in* the play. Stuff in dreams and in daydreams. Sometimes my thought processes appear to be directed by will - making plans and sequencing information - what do I need to fix the leaky tap? How do I make lasagne? - and at other times my thoughts come unbidden, and seem to terrorise my observing awareness with their content and persistence.

## Emotions

The world of emotionality is the territory betwixt mind and body. Sometimes seeming to present as more one than the other, but most often containing elements of both. Thoughts and images emerging as a result of capricious and flowing sensations deep within the confines of my body - belly, chest or limbs. More sensations developing as I observe the fantasies and memories in my mind, creating stories and scenarios that further fuel the bubbling brew of sensation that resides within the cauldron of my body. We *label* recognisable emotional constellations of sensation and feeling with words such as anger, grief, joy, fear, anxiety or worry.

When we attempt to examine the reality of our threefold 'anatomy' from a perceptual viewpoint, it's not always that easy to differentiate what constitutes body, emotions and mind as three distinctly separate entities - each seems to interpenetrate and affect the other two to some degree.

## The Impartial Observer

That which I term the Impartial Observer, we could describe as 'pure awareness'. It is that part of "me" which simply notices - without making judgement, comment or analysis. If I feel a pain within my body, the Observer just registers the sensation. My thinking mind may label the sensation as 'good' or 'bad', painful or pleasurable - the Impartial Observer just notices.

I have labelled the Impartial Observer as being different to Mind, simply by virtue of the fact that it is possible to 'notice' one's mental processes - like looking in on the images and conversations of the mind from outside, so to speak.

**Welcoming into our lives the notion of the Impartial Observer may be the most crucial single step that anyone can ever take in the cultivation of wellness.**

Why? Because it is the impartial observer that can notice the sensations of the body, notice the emotional responses and behaviours, and notice the mental processes. Without this noticing, we cannot take a step back, and we may become highly enmeshed in and identified with the drama of our lives, the experiences and difficulties that we encounter and the roles, opinions, and beliefs that we hold and which serve to shape our human identity. Noticing, without judgement, the various aspects of 'who we are' allows us to take a step beyond identification with the events of my life as 'me', my body as 'me' my emotional displays as 'me' or the contents of my mind as 'me'.

This 'stepping back' often initiates a sense of **relief** - a **relaxation** that clears the mind and softens the body. This softening allows us to face the inevitable changes of life and time with ease and grace - **yielding** to change rather than being bowled over by the smallest alteration in our circumstances.

By noticing the interior world of our body, without overreaction or judgement, we allow for a softening around painful or disturbing sensations which arise from excessive tension, or active disease processes that may be occurring within. This kind of softening will *always* promote a healthier state in the body's tissues as the circulation of fluids and materials is encouraged.

By noticing the coming and going of emotions, creating as they do ripples and storms within the mind and displays of movement and expression in the body, and accepting their presence, we can make an accurate appraisal of this motile phenomenon. We can learn to <u>recognise</u> the various internal energies that make up the meteorology of our moods, and respond in a wakeful and intelligent way to that which moves us.

By <u>noticing</u> the content of the mental sphere of our existence, the pictures and plays of mind-stuff, and immediately softening to the sometimes disturbing displays that the mind is capable of, we can begin to make peace with, and mediate between the angels and demons that urge us toward our choice of actions.

*The practice of <u>noticing</u> without excessive judgement of these internal (and external) experiences of our lives will develop within us an intelligent and increasingly accurate RESPONSE. If we do nothing to develop the art of noticing - if we fail to see the importance of cultivating this ability to create a 'gap' between our awareness and the phenomena upon which it alights - namely the sensory experiences of body, emotion and mind - we will be forever REACTING to all that we perceive, often in clunky and unhelpful ways, constantly overcorrecting and bouncing uncontrollably off the walls of our life.*

If we learn to <u>notice</u>, saying....

> "Ah... a dull ache in my leg.."

Then we may respond in an intelligent way, and take rest after ten hours of digging in the garden, saving ourselves the expense of a visit to the back man.

or...

> "Ah... a feeling of rising wild energy in my chest.

Then we may drive on instead of swerving in front of the car that just cut us up on the last roundabout and proceeding to drag the occupant on to the bonnet.

or...

> "Ah...that old familiar craving and a thought that I should have another drink."

Then we may walk out of the pub, prevent a life-changing catastrophe, and retain our driving licence, liberty and reputation.

Ironically, it is the force of *Unravelling* itself that furnishes us with illness, accident and misfortune, in an attempt to alert us to its presence. Paradoxically, it's trying its absolute damnedest at all times to fuel our evolution and freedom from suffering as individuals (and therefore as a species) by constantly urging us onward toward a place that is greater and wider than we have occupied up to now. It urges us to <u>notice</u>, so that we may be increasingly safe and well. The wilful practice of <u>noticing</u>, therefore, is our closest access point to the intelligence offered by the unceasing nudges provided by *Unravelling*.

There is no rest from the process of change and personal evolution. The uncomfortable truth is that we never did, and never will learn *anything* within our comfort zone - the painful lessons were ever the memorable ones! If we are willing to develop our sensitivity via the practice of <u>noticing</u>, however, the uncomfortable edge of our growing will be just that - mildly uncomfortable rather than agonising, shocking or life-threatening. A softness and a yielding in the face of change makes our personal evolution a much more attractive proposition!

## In Good Order?

Each of the three primary aspects of the human 'system' - mind, body, emotions - has its own characteristics. Each aspect is very different to the others, even though they share the same home within a person. The level of 'health' of each aspect is determined primarily by its level of *organisation*. Each aspect can be well-organised and thereby well-functioning according to its nature (its 'anatomy'), or it may be less well-ordered and may demonstrate chaotic and disorganised tendencies. A high level of organisation within each aspect will allow swift and appropriate adaptability in the face of changing circumstance. Poorer levels of organisation in the system may result in poorly coordinated responses, and either excessive, or diminished responsiveness and response-ability.

In a human being, all three aspects are in constant communication and relationship with each other. The more that each aspect shows a high degree of organisation and appropriate levels of order, the better will be the interrelationship with the other two, creating a higher level of functionality and consequent 'wellness' in the whole organism. Every being is unique. Bodies and minds are diverse in their shapes, sizes and complements. The *Unravelling* urge acts through all however, working constantly to bring about the **best possible** function to ensure survival of the organism.

There seems to be a modern myth that we inevitably become less well as we get older. Don't believe it for a moment - it's just an excuse to get out of paying attention. Personally, I intend to do everything in my power to ensure that I exit this world in excellent health! No matter what stage of our lives we find ourselves at, we are either getting weller, or we are getting iller. It can't be both, and we never stay just so, for the only true constant is change itself! In acknowledging the presence of *Unravelling* in our lives, there is **much** that we can do to align ourselves with this boundless help, making **every moment** of our lives a conscious step towards greater wellness and realisation of our unique potential as fully human beings.

So my question, as before, is this: are we helping or hindering this compassionate force? It cares not. Yet, despite our attempts at sabotage, never deserts us.

# ONE

## Aids to Unravelling

*"Look and you will find it - what is unsought will go undetected"*

Sophocles

Within *Aids to Unravelling*, you'll find very little comment on diet, exercise and supplements. I believe that when we tap into the wisdom that is freely offered to us by the *Unravelling* process, we quickly realise that all the information that we require regarding what we need to eat, how often and in what manner we should move our bodies, and which roots we need to chew on to help the engine out occasionally can be found within us, if we should choose to listen up. We are so swamped by conditional guidance around food and exercise choices (most of it based around fad, fashion and corporate marketing) that we may have ceased to tune in to our quiet internal voice of guidance. Our 'animal' has <u>never</u> lost the ability to know what it needs. Trust it.

## Where to begin?

I'm sure that for medical scientists, the attempt to evaluate and understand physiological processes within the human body is somewhat akin to studying the weather. Our internal environment is constantly changing and shifting under our gaze, and seems to offer only a limited degree of predictability in both its day to day behaviour and throughout the course of our lives. Spanners appear in works and curved balls appear from left field with notorious (but unpredictable) regularity (unlike my mixing of metaphors which happens with regular and alarming predictability). The capricious nature of our biology is never more apparent to us as in the sudden onset of illness.

The reductionist viewpoint of traditional Newtonian science has brought us far in our quest for preservation of life. Without it we would have neither pharmacy nor medical technology, both of which have excelled in the rescuing of lives in acute crisis, and allowed an extension of the years available to those in chronic demise. However, whilst our quest to micro-examine the 'mechanism' has produced much magic, it has taken us far away from trusting the human body as a self-regulating system. We have, in pursuing our infatuation with medical progress, put ourselves way out of touch with a whole body of basic and perennial wisdom, that if it were acknowledged, applied and embodied, could bring us to a place where the emphasis is returned to the cultivation of 'wellness', as opposed to 'fighting illness'.

Of course, science is evolving. The new models of understanding offered by those involved in the field of Quantum Physics may well open the way to a far broader understanding of what makes us tick-tock. I have to admit that I found Newton a bit baffling after the ball bearing bit, so consequently, I suspect that me and Einstein are probably forever destined to be uneasy bedfellows. But to be honest I feel quite relieved to have little understanding of particle accelerators and other such fancy knick-knacks, and am quite happy to have acquired a simple and practical model for understanding human health - one which which makes sense of the kind of favourable outcomes that I am witnessing in the day-to-day of my bodywork practice.

So, where do we start in our attempt to get a handle on this complex and wayward human being thingy? Where will we find the portal that will allow us to walk into and explore the world described and circumscribed by our map? The answer has always been there, right before and in our eyes - under and up our noses. Our everyday senses hold the key to our journey.

# BODY

The human body. What a marvel. And yet for some, more of an adversary than a friend. What words would *you* choose to describe your experience of *your* body? Would those words describe the body as if seen by another person from the outside? Beautiful to behold? Repulsive and ugly? Acceptable? Too big, small, wide, narrow, hairy, bald?

Or would you choose words that describe your experience of the sensations heading your way from your physical frame courtesy of your internal radar system? Ecstatic? Comfortable? Uncomfortable? Painful? Agonising?

Or would you pick the type of words that would describe the way that living in your body makes you *feel*? Heavenly? Powerful? Stable? Able? Awkward? Unable? Miserable? Trapped? Cheated? Resentful? Suicidal? I suspect that most people would pick one or more words from each of the three groups.

The body's appearance from the outside, either seen in the mirror by ourselves, or as we imagine it may appear to others, will certainly affect our feelings about the inhabitation of the particular body with which we have been landed. If body pain is a constant companion in our lives, this will also shape our attitude towards our body as being either a reliable and trustworthy companion, or an inescapable foe. From a physiological point of view, pain is a neurological phenomenon - the nerves are always the medium by which pain is drawn to our attention. However, it is useful to separate pain into three types.

Firstly, pain from direct irritation of the nerve. This may happen if pressure is brought directly on to a nerve fibre. For example, *sciatic* pain experienced in the leg may develop as a result of nerve interference. This may occur either at the nerve root, as it issues from the spinal cord through the gap between the vertebral bones in the lower part of the spinal column, or from direct pressure as the nerve winds its way through the muscles of the buttock at the back of the hip joint.

Secondly, we may experience nerve irritation due to deeper destructive processes going on within the organs of the body. The kind of pain brought about say by stomach ulcers, or gall bladder problems. These pains are referred by the disease to other areas of the body - for example, gall bladder issues may present as pain in the area of the shoulder.

My interest and concern over the years in my practice has been with the third category - what I will term *muscular pain*. Let's keep it simple. Stretched muscles hurt. Muscles in contracted spasm hurt. Impacted muscles hurt. Muscles with diminished flow of circulation hurt. And for all of the dreadful pain that people present with, I go to great pains to point out to them that their pain is, for the most part "just muscular". This doesn't go down too well, especially with those who are experiencing the joys of back pain for the first time, having previously had a comfortable and amicable relationship with their body. The experience can be very scary, causing the person to become highly disoriented. The extreme level of pain involved may convince them that they are very badly damaged. So I am in no way trying to play down the discomfort that they are experiencing, merely pointing them toward recognising the *source* of the pain. The good news, as I explain to them, is that because muscles are a *responsive* part of our soft tissue system, disordered muscle tension is always up for improvement!

As we will see later when talking about body alignment, the individual muscles that serve to hold us together and move us around need to be just the right length and thickness - the correct *tone*. If a muscle is already tight by virtue of repetitive overwork, trauma or misalignment of the skeleton, that muscle may (if pushed that little bit too far) *suddenly* retract into a protective spasm, producing out of the blue, all of the pain and immobility that goes with an acute problem. Quite often, the 'straw that breaks the camel's back' will be a minor movement. When the guy sitting in front of me says that he picked up a pencil and his back collapsed, and how the hell could that happen, I tell him that it was *ready* to happen.

Our bodies are very forgiving, and function fairly normally right up to the edge of their operational tolerances, only squeaking and calling a halt to proceedings right at the very last moment! I've often wondered whether this is a bit of a design fault. It might be useful if we had a little meter with an arrow that creeps up as we are going about our business, a red DANGER area as we're heading for 'ping' territory, and a little hooter that goes off when we are thirty seconds from going over the edge. The thing is, we **do** have such a mechanism available. It's a network of nerve fibres situated throughout the body, that constantly feeds back to us levels of sensation related to discomfort and fatigue in our muscular system. Most of my clients who have gone 'ping' complain like hell that they never got any warning of the impending malfunction. However, upon further questioning, most admit to having **overridden** their internal information feedback system, often for quite a period of time in relation to fatigue and discomfort.

The body is very smart. *Unravelling* always has our best interests at heart. It is a champion of our survival. It will tell us when to stop. If our personal will <u>overrides</u> a clear message to desist, then, sorry boys, 'ping' it is. *Unravelling* cares not. Its only concern is our continuing well-being - it's not bothered if the lawn doesn't get cut before it starts to rain...

## Pain as wake-up call

If one thing has become clear to me during my time in practice, it is this:

THE PRIMARY FUNCTION OF PAIN
IS TO ATTRACT OUR ATTENTION

This sounds a bit like a case of stating the obvious. Of course pain will draw our attention... it bloody well hurts! But to suggest that somehow this pain which is SO inconvenient to me (as I can't go to the gym for the fourteenth time this week) is somehow helpful to my well-being? How dare you suggest that, you awful New-Ager sitting there spouting your silly philosophy.... why, I'm going to come over there RIGHT now and give you a piece of my mind (but unfortunately I can't seem to get out of this chair). Hmmm... you may have a point.

Mind and Body were ever uneasy bedfellows. The body is, of course, in complete control of proceedings. When it gets laid low for one reason or another, "we" (as the inhabitant of said body) have no choice but to go down with it, usually blaming it at the time for its errant ways (silly body). The body is HUGELY intelligent, and only ever acts in an *intelligent* way. Its sole concern is to PRESERVE ITSELF, and whenever we drive it beyond its ability to function well, it will start to quietly pull the rug out from under our will.

So how does this process unfold?

First tiredness.
*"No problem. More coffee please".*
Then a snuffly cold
*"Of course I'm going to work. Have we got any paracetamol?"*
Then a back problem
*"Super-strength paracetamol?"*
Then headaches
*"Must be the cheese - I'll give that up.*

Then digestive upsets

"Zantac please."

Then constipation

"Better put some laxatives in with that lot. Thanks Mr Pharmacist."

Then gallstones

"Keyhole surgery - out in a day - wonderful! I'll make it to the gym tonight."

Then arthritis

"I promise to cut the gym down to thirteen times this week."

Then palpitations

"I need the downers Doc..."

Then depression

"Maybe the uppers as well while you're at it."

Then the vague non-specific pain symptoms and associated lethargy

"Ah NOW we'll try some Acupuncture - that'll keep me going in the manner to which I have become accustomed!"

Then.......well, then probably something a little more chronic and possibly a wee bit terminal.

"Oops... should have got to bed a bit earlier in the first place. Do we get another go...? No...? Oh well."

Our mind is very conditioned to organise our lives in order to preserve *the image of how we see ourselves to be...*

> "I am a FIT person so I WILL go to the gym!"

...and will (often quite blindly) lead our body toward endeavours that serve to perpetuate that image. The body's needs often come a sorry second place. Ever since the seventeenth century, when philosopher René Descartes stated that he thought (and therefore he was), the body has been generally consigned to the naughty step and treated as some sort of wayward and malfunctioning machine.

We'll revisit all of this again later, but for now, let's get down to the task of intelligently re-inhabiting this lovely squishy suit.

# AIDS FOR BODY

## Bringing Attention to the Body

The instruction "listen!" is most akin to the instruction "bring attention to...". It's quite easy to "listen" to the sensations in the body. The heartbeat can be felt ("listening" via sensation) and may even be heard audibly as a pulse in the chest or the head. If we are very quiet, we can sense the rushing of blood around the vessels of the arterial system. By bringing attention to the belly, we may feel (and occasionally hear) the crawling gurgle and chug of the digestive tract. If we are quieter still, we may register a sort of tingling sparkling hum that pervades the whole of our internal body space.

If we choose to bring attention to various body parts - trunk, limbs, head, various individual joints, organs or digits, we will find that each part is inhabited by a very specific sensation. The area around the heart (behind the left-hand side of the breastbone) definitely has a different feel to the area inhabited by the liver (on the right-hand side at the lower margin of the front of the ribcage). The head may feel very alive. The belly could feel very far away, or maybe the pelvis seems quite absent to our enquiring attention. Left and right limbs could feel internally very different.

To take a 'tour' around the body using your directed intention as a vehicle for your awareness is an invaluable Aid To Unravelling. The primary reason for this is that *your very attention to a body area will improve the circulation of blood to that location.*

This idea is based on a basic tenet of Chinese Taoist philosophy, namely that...

> *"..the blood follows the qi (energy), and the qi follows the attention."*

The well-being of all of the body's tissues relies on an effective blood supply. The blood brings oxygen and removes waste products. Blood is the physiological courier of the *Unravelling* urge.

### EXERCISE 01 - ATTENTION TO THE HAND

Try this. Hold one of your hands out in front of you. Keeping your hand still, gaze very softly at your hand and gently put all of your attention into the sensations that you feel in your hand. After a very short time, you will probably notice that your hand starts to tingle. Keep this up for a minute or so. If you look at your hand you may find that it has become flushed, or blotchy on the palm. These changes are due to an increase in blood circulation, *effected simply by virtue of you directing your attention to your hand*. Can you imagine the benefits to your health and well-being if you were to do a ten minute tour of the major sites of interest within your own body every single day?

# Bringing Attention to the Breath

How are you breathing right now?

Are you breathing right now...?

(We can assume that you are, otherwise the likelihood of us having this conversation would be quite slim.)

We can divide the activities of the human biological system into two categories - those activities that we are able to facilitate by way of VOLUNTARY control, and those that operate in an INVOLUNTARY way. For example, we can voluntarily wave a hand in the air, but would find it difficult to wilfully alter the rate of urine production by the kidneys. These involuntary processes will of course alter in relation to what we do - the heart rate will definitely increase if we choose to run up a hill, and more time in the bathroom will inevitably follow on from drinking six pints of fine English ale - but without those accompanying activities, your average Joe cannot alter such bodily processes via an act of will. Our breathing, however, is an interesting case, falling as it does into both categories.

Ignored, our breathing will continue to happen at the required rate, even when we are asleep. If we choose though, to bring our attention to the breath we can alter the rate of breathing - speed it up, slow it down, or even suspend it for a short time. This is because the muscles that facilitate the mechanics of breathing - primarily the *diaphragm muscle* - are available to being activated by voluntary control as well as being regulated automatically.

Try it out now. Close your eyes and bring you attention to your breathing. This is the breathing rate that has been trundling along nicely all on its ownsome whilst you've been reading these pages. Once your attention is nicely settled on the breath, speed it up or slow the rate a little. Then hold your breath for a few seconds. When you have finished and take your attention away from the breath and back to the book, your breath will not stop. The activity returns to the jurisdiction of your involuntary control systems. Smart eh?

The diaphragm muscle separates the contents of the thoracic cavity above (primarily heart and lungs), from the abdominal cavity (mainly digestive system). It's a bit like a loose drum skin that sits horizontally in the form of a a dome between the two body sections. On inhalation, the muscle contracts and the dome becomes taut and flatter. This draws down the lungs (which are attached by intermediary tissues to the upper surface of the diaphragm) and the lungs fill with air. As the muscle relaxes, exhalation occurs, and the gas in the lungs is expelled. This rhythmic contraction and relaxation of the diaphragm also has a health-promoting effect on the contents of the abdominal cavity, by rhythmically massaging the organs of the digestive system. The evidence of diaphragm movement can be seen (most obviously in animals and also tiny children, who have much less disordered breathing than adults) as the belly expands and falls back gently with each breath. This expansion of the belly is caused by the slight displacement of the abdominal organs as the diaphragm contracts and descends.

We do, however, have another breathing mechanism. This is called accessory breathing, or 'chest breathing'. As the name suggests, this kicks in when we need a bit more air. When we are exercising vigorously and require a greater intake of oxygen, the lungs are caused to expand their volume even more with each breath, by way of a lifting and expansion of the rib cage itself. This primarily involves an elevation of the breastbone (sternum) by the muscles on the front of the neck, and results in the classic 'heaving' chest of that person who's just missed the Number 42 bus.

As the name suggests, this mechanism kicks in when we need a bit more air. When we are exercising vigorously and require a greater intake of oxygen, the lungs are caused to expand their volume even more with each breath, by way of a lifting and expansion of the rib cage itself. This primarily involves an elevation of the breastbone (sternum) by the muscles on the front of the neck, and results in the classic 'heaving' chest of that person who's just missed the Number 42 bus.

Now, with regard to our general well-being, here's the rather interesting and **very important bit** (so put that packet of choccie biccies down just for a minute).

*Stress* (you know that one), which generally produces a mild and ongoing version of the physiological effects associated with what we call *fear* or *anxiety*, brings about changes in our normal relaxed breathing pattern.

    * When we are scared, anxious or stressed, the action of the diaphragm lessens, and we begin to **chest breathe**.

    * When we are scared, anxious or stressed the **rhythm**, **depth** and **speed** of our breath alters.

    * When we are scared, anxious or stressed we may start to **retain** or **hold** our breath.

It goes without saying that these effects will seriously alter biochemical and hormonal processes within our system (oxygen levels will be low, adrenaline levels high) but the big deal for me as a bodyworker is the serious detrimental effect that chronic chest breathing has on the **postural mechanics** and **alignment** of the body.

## In people who are <u>continually</u> stressed (that's you, by the way and about 100% of the people you know), *accessory*, or chest breathing becomes the predominant breathing mechanism.

Read the statement above a few times. It's in **big** letters for a very good reason. Now put the book down, go and have a cup of tea and come back and read it a few more times. Come back to it every day and read it again. Copy it and pin it up on the wall of every room in your house. Set it up as a screen saver on your computer - paint it on the inside of your eyelids. In fact do anything to make sure that this bit of information becomes permanently installed in your memory bank.

**If you value your life (which I'm sure you do) then this piece of information may well be the most important thing that you have ever received.**

So what's the big deal? Well, the issue is that the mechanical action of habitual chest breathing sets up abnormal muscle tensions in the whole body that eventually take the body a *very* long way away from good functioning.

Once the body structure has become chronically altered and compromised in this way, chest breathing becomes the default action. This means that even if the **sources** of stress and anxiety disappear from our lives, we will still feel stressed and anxious, as we have adopted all of the biomechanical and physiological characteristics of a stress-ridden being.

I was recently asked...

"If you could give one practice, or offer one piece of advice that would go the furthest toward creating positive change in the state of a person's health, what would it be?"

Not a single doubt in my heart...
ABDOMINAL BREATHING PRACTICE.
Period.

## EXERCISE 02 ABDOMINAL BREATHING

Try this.

Lie down on your bed. Spend a minute or two just settling down.

Put one hand on your belly and one hand on your chest.

Allow all the breath to leave your body.

NOW...

Take a SLOW and medium size breath in (through your nose if possible).

You should feel movement under your hands as your belly and/or chest rise toward the ceiling.

Breathe out in an unforced way allowing all the breath to gently leave your body - the belly and chest will sink naturally toward the bed.

Slowly repeat the process above a dozen or so times - take plenty of time and notice what's happening under your hands, especially the hand on your belly.

You may find that your belly movement is quite full, or it may be absent, with all the action going on up in the chest. If there's not much happening at the belly end, repeat the process above and tune in to the small movement in the belly.

NOW

Transfer both hands to the belly, and start to focus your attention into the movement of the belly as you breathe in and out.

Begin to disallow any movement in the chest as you breathe in, and you should find that you get more raising of the belly, which you will be able to feel under your hands.

You are now starting to use the diaphragm muscle more fully.

Once you have made a little progress and can feel the movement of the belly under your hands becoming a little more full and responsive, remove your attention from the sensation of your breathing and just rest gently for five minutes.

If you continue with this practice you should find that you are able to take control of the belly filling process to a deeper and deeper extent, the experience being that you are expanding into the lower part of your belly, and into the pelvis. You may also feel that you can expand your abdomen with the breath in all directions, like a barrel.

The particular exercise is definitely best performed whilst lying down - maybe before going to sleep at night. You may only get to ten breaths before dropping off! In this case it's probably best to do the practice earlier in the day (and also do it at night as a way-of-getting-to-sleep thing!).


## ** *NOTE ABOUT BREATHING EXERCISES*

As with all breathing exercises, it's best to start GENTLY and feel your way into a new way of being over a period of days or weeks. Start small, and gradually extend the practice, both in terms of...

- the *volume* of the breath
- the *number of times* that you may practice a new exercise per week
- the *length of time* that you practice the exercise for.

ALWAYS breathe slowly when performing breathing exercises. There is a possibility that when you begin to change your breathing style you may experience a mild dizziness, as the oxygenation levels within your body go through some positive alterations. For this reason, always spend a couple of minutes breathing with no particular focus before moving from a horizontal position to a sitting position, and always sit for a minute prior to standing up and walking around.

## The Outbreath

Now that we have firmly established the importance of the use of the diaphragm when inhaling, we need to turn our attention to the exhale - the outbreath. Ideally, the outbreath should be a very relaxed and passive affair, and be *complete* without forcing. This takes the ribcage and the diaphragm to a suitable state of relaxation prior to the next inbreath.

## *EXERCISE 03 BREATHING OUT PRACTICE*

Try this.

Lie on your front diagonally across your bed. Have your head hanging off the corner of the bed, with your forehead supported on something soft which is a bit lower than the bed (a low stool with a cushion on will do). Get your arms comfortable, either by your sides or hanging down on to the floor or some support.

Spend a couple of minutes bringing your attention to your breathing. Settle yourself into a nice soft breathing rhythm. Ensure that you are breathing into your belly - using your diaphragm muscle. If you are, then your inbreath should push your body upwards away from the surface of the bed very softly.

Then begin to focus on the outbreath.

Allow the outbreath to be very passive - just let gravity take your body and allow your ribcage to deflate under its own weight. As you breathe out, let your shoulder blades, shoulders, arms, hands, neck, head and face all surrender to gravity.

After a few minutes, begin to allow a little pause - maybe five seconds - at the end of each outbreath. See if there's any extra tension in your upper body that you can let go of.

After a few more minutes, put in the occasional thirty second pause at the end of the outbreath. Bring your awareness to your body and just let go into the stillness.

During the pause, notice any subtle tension in the ribcage, or breastbone area that you may wish to surrender to gravity.

During the pause, bring your awareness to any uncomfortable feelings of anxiety that may arise within you. Simply notice.

During the pause notice any pleasant feelings of serenity or peacefulness that may be generated within your body.

During the pause, see if there are any physical sensations within your body that call to your attention.

Spend a minute bringing your breath back to a normal working rhythm and carefully get fully on to your bed and turn on to your back.

Spend a couple more minutes breathing 'normally' before making your way back to the vertical position.

## Breath-holding on the inhale

The lungs never completely empty themselves of air, but retention of an abnormal portion of the breath is a very common habit. If you think about it, breathing out is quite a risky proposition. How can you be certain, as you give up the breath on exhalation, that there'll actually be another inbreath? It's a matter of developing faith, as a result of experience.

For many who have (due to illness or trauma) lost the trust in their body as a reliable ally, *any* automatic body function may be regarded with suspicion. The body exists 'down there' somewhere below the neck, and of course it's only a matter of time before it does something unpredictable or dangerous. For these people, *control* over their body and its functions becomes a major issue. They may be excessively regimented with regard to exercise, and fastidious in their dietary and hygiene practices. There may be an emphasis on 'body-image' - the right kind of shape or weight. Going way beyond any 'normal' level of interest in their well-being, they develop a vain and deluded crusade to shape, and keep tabs on the wayward world of their own physiological processes.

As I pointed out earlier, the breathing mechanism is unusual inasmuch as it is available to both voluntary command *and* autonomic involuntary control. For those who wish to exercise a level of over-control upon their long-suffering but compliant frame, their breathing is a primary target. In this individual there will usually be a tendency toward chest breathing - the sensations in the abdomen created by the normal action of the diaphragm may bring the person a little too close for comfort to the disturbing contents of their belly! This kind of excessive control will also show up in the outbreath, manifesting as a tendency to retain a portion of the breath, reflecting a deeply-held fear of 'letting go' and of placing trust in the intelligence that so obviously governs their bodily functions.

I have observed a curious thing in some people. They actually stop breathing when they are listening to someone else speaking to them, holding the breath whilst the lungs are full. I have quizzed people about this one and I suspect that the habit originates from childhood, or from experiences in education. Having a scary guardian or teacher 'in your face' on a regular basis would be the kind of thing that would set up this kind of pattern. This type of breath holding is also seen as a result of hypervigilance. Children who were brought up in the presence of unpredictable others, maybe suffering regularly at the hands of a temper-driven guardian or sibling, learn to be constantly on the look-out (or listen-out) for trouble, quietening their own internal processes such as breathing so as to heighten their awareness of their surroundings.

Because the outbreath is a passive action, driven to an extent by a surrender, any attempt to retain the breath demands enormous muscular effort. The breath-retaining person will show the pattern of tension in the body commensurate with chest breathing, and also an *over-inflation* of the rib cage.

Structurally speaking, a life of breath retention is evidenced by a permanent over-expansion in the upper ribcage. Our ability to reach out into the world is facilitated on the physical level by way of our arms. The freedom of the upper limb is governed by the ability of the whole shoulder girdle - collarbone, shoulder blade and limb - to move with freedom on the upper part of the back. This girdle mechanism relates to the body by way of a network of multidirectional muscles. The only bony connection is between the central end of the collarbone and the top of the breastbone. Consequently, if the upper rib cage is in a state of permanent expansion, the freedom and potential of the shoulder girdle can become severely limited. It is a bit like trying to fit a tent canvas over a frame that is one size to big for it. The ability of the muscles to retain correct length, tone and function is obviously diminished, chronic discomfort in the upper back, shoulders and neck being an inevitable result.

## The neck, the throat and the voice... expression and creativity

I never cease to be amazed by the neck and its associated structures. If you ever get a chance to look at an anatomy book, find a picture of a cross-section of the neck. How the hell does so much stuff fit into there and still retain the ability to work as well as it does? Food goes down (and occasionally comes up). Air goes in, changed air comes out. Food goes down the right hole. Air doesn't for the most part go down the food hole. There's support for a whole mastication mechanism, and the anchor for something that trebles as a taste sensing thingy, a modifier of shape to facilitate speech, and something to stick out at traffic wardens (or is that just me?). Blood goes up, feeding the brain, and blood comes down. There's a scaffolding to support the (considerable) weight of the skull and its contents (which doubles as a passageway for the nerve superhighway of the spinal cord) and a whole gamut of associated guy ropes and strings and pulleys to move the head around. And whilst all this is going on, the diva can stand on the operatic stage and hold a perfectly formed top C with uber-controlled vibrato for the best part of twenty seconds... just phenomenal.

You can clearly see that for the well-being of these structures and complex functions, excessive tension in the neck is HIGHLY undesirable, and correct alignment of the head's position on top of the neck, crucial. So again I implore you - abandon the path of accessory and take up abdominal breathing practice as a life-extender and a potential life-saver!

There are two characteristics of human physiology (big brain aside) that place us aside from all of the other species on this planet. It is these two that hold the key to our 'success' in the grand scheme of things. One is the opposing thumb, which allows us to dexter away to our heart's content, making tools, holding pens, and fashioning bombs and guns and spaceships. The second is the voice. It is our voice that allows us, via the medium of language, to put forth our will, and shape the world as we wish to see it. To hold the breath (whether consciously or not) demands another muscular feat - the stopping up of the throat. This is possibly the most detrimental act that we can ever inflict upon ourselves. Not only does it have a massively destructive effect upon our physiology, but it threatens to put a lid on our personal happiness by discouraging the expression of need via the voice.

During the more Neanderthal stage of our evolution, it was fire and club that kept the predator at bay. These days, I am far less likely to be stalked by a sabre-tooth thingy of any persuasion and, in my part of the world at least, seem to be unbothered by humans intent on causing me bodily harm. Creating boundaries by the use of tooth and claw seems to be a skill that I am unlikely to have to draw upon. These days, the lines are drawn and defended by way of the spoken word.

The simplest words often have the greatest power. The words 'yes' and 'no' are good examples. 'Yes' invites something in. Stating 'No' leaves the other person in no doubt about our intentions. For some (and I count myself in here), the word 'no' did not always come easily. Upon receiving a request, I habitually delayed my gut response of

*"Sorry. No way. You've got to be kidding."*

and... well would you look at that... the complete opposite came out of my mouth!

*"Of course I don't mind darling. I may have been asleep, and be completely exhausted, have to be up at the crack of dawn and could probably name a million and one other things of greater import than this right now... yes I know that it's two in the morning and it's snowing but I'm MORE than happy to go and get the laundry (that you forgot to bring in) off the washing line... "*

To say 'yes' to my own needs, and to say 'no' to others - me first and them second - always went a bit against the grain and I got myself into a deep and intractable habit. I know from years of automatically responding in this way how much disorder this habit brought to the structure of my neck muscles and associated functions, every delayed and diverted honest response creating a micro-stopping up of my outbreath via a closed throat.

My unconscious motivation for saying 'yes' to others, even when I would really have liked to have said 'no' was to ensure that they would stick around, saving me from my fear of abandonment. Sacrificing my own needs seemed a small price to pay. Trouble was, the situation was unsustainable, so eventually losing the company of those to whom I fibbed was inevitable, as each dishonest response set another tiny seed of resentment in my core. Reluctance, conscious or otherwise, to state needs on this very basic level will ALWAYS result in disorder of the breathing mechanism. The perilous path of unspoken truths...

## Manner of speaking

Under ideal conditions, the basic feature of the breath is that it be CONTINUOUS. Even at the ends of the in- and outbreaths, there is no actual pause. A bit like a pendulum at the end of each swing - if you were to magnify the pendulum bob to a greater and greater degree, you would find that the *actual point* where it stopped in space would become ever more difficult to find.

The speaking voice should modulate ON TOP of this continuous, full and easy breath. The breath is the stage upon which the spoken word can dance in all of its beauty. If a person's style of speech DICTATES the depth and speed of the breath, trouble may ensue. If the delivery of speech is fast, with little in the way of pauses between sentences (or even words!), it is likely that the person is snatching their breath via the accessory breathing mechanism - gasping through the mouth, and not utilising the diaphragm. This style of speech is likely to create a person who uses chest-breathing as a default, even when they are silent.

To breathe through the nose using the diaphragm to inhale, to deliver one's speech by way of a full, natural exhalation, and then to recharge by way of another diaphragmatic inbreath, demands a pause in speech ................................... quite a considerable pause.

When we hear a great orator in full flow, it is often their use of pauses that really makes the impression. During a lecture, when someone speaks with great conviction and clarity on a subject with which the audience is in agreement, the pause is a luxury in which he or she can bask, knowing that there will be no interruption. To hear people pausing this much in conversation is rare. We may worry that our pause offers the other person an undesirable chance to jump in with their own words, and ruin the opportunity to get our point across! Whenever I come across someone who has developed a gasping, machine-gun style of speaking, further investigation usually reveals that they are, or have at some point in their lives lived in an environment where interruption was common, and they had to fight to get themselves heard.

## The vanished breath...

Much of what I have examined so far with regard to the breath, relates to the cultivation of diaphragm use, encouraging us away from chest breathing as our default mechanism. Although the habit of stopping, or holding the breath is most commonly seen in relation to retention of the *inbreath*, there are those who have developed a tendency to hold at the end of the outbreath. In this case, they will actually be using the diaphragm to breathe, but in an extremely minimal way. From the outside, it may appear as if they are hardly breathing at all. There is often a stillness about the person which seems very guarded, and they may be easily irritated by outside disturbance. The rib cage appears very narrow, the chest sunken. The diminishment of breath volume has obvious implications for our health - oxygen uptake and disposal of carbon dioxide, will both be affected in a detrimental way.

It is useful to appreciate the rib cage as a 'sprung' mechanical system. As we inhale, and inflate the lungs, the springy cage expands its volume, stretching the muscular and soft tissue suit that contains it. The exhale in this situation can be quite passive, as the natural elasticity of the system returns the rib cage to its initial size. We have seen how a continual holding of the inbreath results in a rib cage that becomes permanently expanded - the muscles stretched and unable to regain that natural elasticity to bring the ribcage back to 'neutral'. A forced outbreath, where we forcibly expel the air in the lungs to a greater degree than would naturally occur, elicits the elastic nature of the rib cage in the *opposite* direction. If we force exhalation to its very limit and then let go, there will be an automatic inhale to bring the system back to the neutral position.

To hold on the outbreath takes some effort - much more wilful effort than retaining the inbreath, and results in a far deeper level of chronic tension within the core of the body. Eventually, the ribcage loses its natural elasticity, and the ability to express a full and natural breath becomes a thing of the past. Poor oxygen uptake and a 'depressed' chest may reflect in the person's character, making them listless, and a little less than enthusiastic about their lives.

# Alignment

Alignment of the body is one of the primary factors in determining good health or otherwise. It is best to begin our discussion at the subject of alignment from the perspective of the deepest structure within the body - the skeleton.

Bone is a remarkable substance. It is light, yet tensile (which means that it can suffer quite extreme torsion without breaking). Also, bone is ALIVE. It is constantly being destroyed and renewed via the action of cells designed for the job. Bone is laid down in response to forces placed upon it by the pull of muscles. This is why the skeleton has 'knobbly bits' - anchors at the sites of attachment of major muscles. Individual bones within the skeleton will change their shape over a period of time dependent upon the habitual style of movement and muscle tensions within an individual. The skeleton has several functions, but its primary job is as a mobile support system.

## Gravity

Everything that exists on this Earth is subjected to the gravitational field that draws all on the surface (and things flying through the air) toward the centre of the planet. No matter where you are on the globe, gravity will always be (getting you) DOWN.

It has been said by many that man was never designed to stand vertically, and that many of the ailments that afflict the back in particular are due to some flaw in the blueprint - maybe the engineer had a bit of a hangover the day that *homo sapiens* passed across the drawing board.

Do you know what I say to that? PAH! That's what!

If you have a good look at a picture of the human skeleton, you will see that it has "I LOVE GRAVITY" scrawled all over its beautiful architecture.

The skeleton has many joints, some freely movable (such as the knee and shoulder) which in concert allow locomotion of the body through space, and give us the ability to reach out and shape the world. Other joints, that have a very much smaller range of motion are primarily involved with the way that FORCES travel through the core of the skeletal system, dealing with shock-absorption, and maintenance of the stability and posture of the whole body during movement.

Each joint within the skeleton has a range of movement that is decided by the structure of the joint - the range of movement of the shoulder joint will be much greater than the range of movement of the tiny joints present within the central part of the foot - but at best, the resting position of EVERY skeletal joint whilst standing will be at an anatomically correct position. If this is the case, then we will observe what we could call an 'ideal' (I avoid using the word 'perfect') standing posture. The bone surfaces in each joint are separated by a film of synovial fluid within the joint, so in the ideal standing posture, the body is literally 'floating' on a sea of fluid.

In this situation, when the mechanical forces are travelling efficiently through the *absolute anatomical centre* of each joint within the skeleton, there is only an *absolute minimum* of necessary tension present within the muscular system to maintain verticality. Consequently, the 'lined-up' body, being pulled down by gravity on to the solid surface of the floor, will receive an opposite UPTHRUST force, which effectively neutralises the body weight, creating the grace and lightness of being that is our birthright as human beings - MAGIC! In this scenario, gravity becomes our ally, and lifts us effortlessly to great things.

Of course, this ideal is very rarely seen - most people are wonky to one degree or another. This wonkiness is created by deep levels of muscular tension within the body, caused by trauma, accidents, stress, poor breathing habits (as we have discussed), repetitive use of one side of the body, and postural habits. Because the skeleton has so many joints, the whole body is able to compensate for local distortion, and the person can function, albeit in a compromised way. However, misalignment as described will set the seeds for future trouble. This is because in a misaligned body, the skeleton can no longer take on its true role of support system - the vertical stacking of body segments (head, chest, pelvis and legs) has now vanished. This body will now start to BRACE against the force of gravity by developing chronic tension, firstly in the *deep postural muscles* responsible for fine-tuning stance and movement, and later on the bigger and more exterior *gymnastic muscles* whose job it is to initiate and sustain movement.

GRAVITY NOW BECOMES OUR ADVERSARY (boo... hiss... underneath you!) and the downward direction becomes culturally mythologised as the road to hell...

So what are the consequences of this insidiously developing and undesirable body tension? Well, let's turn it round first off and look at the kind of experience that may be had by someone inhabiting a body with 'ideal' vertical posture.

- Because our body is in 'neutral', the initiation and performance of movement will feel easy and light.
- We will experience a reduced level of muscular discomfort
- Body to limb, and hand to eye co-ordination will be good.
- The ability to deal effectively with sudden and unexpected changes in our environment will be enhanced
- We will have more stamina, as the blood supply to the muscles will be improved due to to their relaxed and toned condition.

- As we are expending very little energy in our ongoing relationship with gravity, we will have much more energy available to us for the other things in life.
- The focus of breathing will be returned to the diaphragm, with all of the benefits that have been discussed previously.

And the health benefits?

- Improved circulation
- Improved nervous system function and transmission
- Improved digestive and assimilation function
- Improved waste disposal
- Improved bone condition

etc. etc.

Need I go on? The fact is that when alignment of the skeleton is improved, usually by a combination of therapeutic help, training and awareness, and the bones are encouraged to return to their role and duty as bearers of the body weight whilst in a vertical position, EVERY aspect of the human function is enlivened, and drawn toward the very best that it is capable of being. With our feet deeply and passionately connected to the floor, and our head eagerly reaching up to the stars, the *Unravelling* force can reach deeply into and through our body's systems. The beneficial effects of the deep and *purposeful* relaxation encouraged by a vertical and aligned skeletal structure go way beyond the physical and physiological aspects of the body. The benefits on *mind* and *emotions* we will come to later.

## Cultivating verticality...

...is a PRACTICE.

We are moving and ever changing beings. We cannot create and sustain a static verticality - we have better things to do in our lives than become like a tree! However, static, or still standing practice is one of the most successful ways of leading us TOWARD a greater and ongoing appreciation of body alignment, and a fruitful alliance with the ever-present gravitational force of our planet.

When we practise abdominal breathing, as described earlier, we could do it formally - maybe before going to sleep at night. Twenty breaths. Done. Then just let it go. We don't need to be monitoring our breath all day to check whether or not we're getting it right. The reason for this, is that diaphragmatic breathing is the body's NATURAL preference, and if given half a chance will go there as default. All we need to do is take our attention to this option once a day, and our body will grab the opportunity and run with it. Prove this to yourself by trying it over a couple of weeks - you'll find that it's absolutely sound theory! Once set in place, it's very unlikely that we'll ever return to a fully disordered state. If, maybe under stressful conditions, we do start to go back to chest breathing, we hopefully will have developed enough awareness to notice the change pretty much straight away, and we can apply corrective measures.

Similarly with cultivating verticality. Clients often express surprise once their body has been realigned during bodywork treatment, that it has any chance of staying in that improved position - they generally assume that a return to misalignment is inevitable. I try and impress upon them that the body retains true alignment because it LIKES to be balanced. It grabs hold of the new alignment, matches it up with the reliable vector of the ever-constant gravitational force and maintains itself - just as its design dictates.

I consider bodywork to be primarily an EDUCATIONAL process. Intervention is not the major part, although generally is necessary to a greater or lesser degree. If people are either not willing, or can't muster enough curiosity to engage with the process of cultivating awareness with regard to their body's movements and repetitive patterns, then creating and maintaining positive change can be much more difficult. As the old saying goes...

*"If you always do what you always did then you'll always get what you always got"*

Best do something different then I reckon...

It's worth stating here that successful realignment of the body is <u>always</u> a process, which takes time, and demands patience, awareness and care from the owner. You set it straight, it slips back again. You set it straight again, and it slips back a bit less. Eventually, with good habits, a bit of luck and a following wind balance is restored.

Those who then become curious regarding the practice of cultivating relaxed verticality, and start to deal with their dodgy postural habits and poor breathing practices, and who go on to ACTIVELY and CONSCIOUSLY engage with verticality practice... well they just seem to get weller and weller and weller.

## EXERCISE 04 - STILL STANDING PRACTICE

Try this.

Take time to stand for a moment. On a flat surface. Feet parallel and about shoulder-width apart.

Bring your attention to your feet, and to the nine points of contact on each foot, which are...
Heel,
ball behind the big toe,
outside edge,
and five toes resting lightly on the floor.
Become aware of the apex point of the arches in the centre of the sole of the foot. This is the ninth point.
Allow the foot to soften, and feel the ninth point gently softening toward the floor, even though there will be no appreciable physical movement.
Adjust your position until all eighteen points of contact are evenly loaded.

Flex your knees very slightly (not so far that your knee becomes forward of the toes).

Hang your arms down by your side, palms facing in whichever direction they fall.

Take a gentle breath into your belly.
As you exhale, allow your chest to soften and drop.
Pause for a moment.
Again, breathe gently into your belly and soften the chest on exhalation.

Turn your pelvis under you slightly as if to point your tailbone to the space between your heels.
Relax the buttocks and pelvic floor.

Look straight forward with a gentle gaze into the half-distance.
Tuck in your chin slightly and place the tip of your tongue behind your top front teeth.

Feel and imagine the back of the neck being stroked upward and lengthened.
Feel the top of the head being drawn up toward the sky as if by a single hair on your crown.

From this point on keep the knees at the same degree of flexion - no less, no more

Now return your attention to your feet and let go in the arch of your foot - just allow gravity to act. You may notice a temperature change in your feet.

Relax the calf and allow the lower leg to settle on to the ankle joint.
Same for the thigh and upper leg on to the knee.
Take about fifteen seconds for each of these stages to occur.

Relax all the muscles in the pelvis and allow the pelvis to settle on to the hip joints
and the torso to drop on to the base of the back.

Again sink the chest but do not allow the spine to slump.

Check the turning under of the pelvis and allow the lower spine to lengthen and settle.

Relax the arms and hands, and allow the shoulder girdle to settle gently on to the top of the rib cage.

Check the slight chin-in and allow the neck to settle on to the spine, and the skull to settle on to the neck.

LET GO
Don't allow any more knee flexion and don't let the spine slump.
LET GO

LET GO

Let go and let gravity do its thing. It will effortlessly thrust you up as you LET GO and allow the floor to receive the weight of your body through your bones.

LET GO

This is today's standing position.

As you stand, allow your attention to be drawn to any area of your body that calls to you by way of sensation.

Notice how your body during your practice may twitch and tremble, as muscle groups let go and readjust the alignment of the body segments.

Notice the appearance and disappearance of subtle vibrations within the body, the location of which may be hard to pin down.

As you take more weight into the skeleton, notice how hidden pain may appear as the long suffering major muscle groups begin to relax and flood with blood and life and sensation as they have a well-earned rest from holding you up and fighting gravity!
LET GO

Notice how it feels to stand in your bones.....

Over the years, my personal preference for exercises and practices has gravitated toward things that are SIMPLE and EFFECTIVE. Making changes will always take TIME, so I've never been fond of anything that promises the offer of a quick fix. Effective practices are very often accompanied by a little discomfort. Now I'm not into masochism in any shape or form, but as I have already said, I believe that it's nigh on impossible to learn anything whilst you're in your comfort zone.

Even in the absence of standing practice, basic postural hygiene should be observed as follows:

WHILST SITTING
• Crossing one leg over the other is an obvious no-no.
• Sit toward the back of any chair that you're in. If the base is too deep from front to back, put a cushion behind you, so that the back of your pelvis is supported, thus preventing the pelvis from tipping backwards.
• Have your feet flat on the floor. If the chair's too tall, use a foot support.

- Having done all of that, let your upper body (shoulders/head) find a relaxed resting position. If you're bottom end is sorted, then your top half will look after itself!

## AT THE COMPUTER

- Ensure that your chair will insert under your desk space (chair arms often disallow this). This gets you closer to your work and discourages 'perching' on the edge of the seat.

- Obviously, make sure that your computer is lined up straight in front of you, the monitor is far enough away to be visually comfortable, and the mouse is close.

**It's SO important to have the feet flat on the floor whilst sitting** - this is another one of those things that I would like everyone to have burned into their minds as one of the Top Ten Tips for a long and healthy life. Legs are heavy - whoever you are. If you're sitting in a chair and your feet are picked up off the floor, either tucked up under the chair or balancing on the toes in some way, then you are elevating a significant proportion of your own body weight (your legs) using primarily the muscles of your low back. Try this. Sit in the back of a simple chair with your feet flat on the floor, relax into the seat and then VERY SLOWLY start to lift both feet off the floor at the same time. You'll feel quite clearly where the muscular origin of this action is - right in the centre of the abdomen. Tension in this area whilst sitting makes correct breathing very unlikely.

Many have a tendency to "lift" the body when sitting - 'sitting up' to create what they believe to be 'good posture'. This is misleading. If whilst doing this you get someone to put a straight-edge vertically against your back from the sitting surface to the middle of your back you will feel the exaggerated convex curve in the low back region - the back curving away from the straight-edge.

This 'sitting up' position may develop as a result of dance training, or have its roots in the historical terrorising guidance of some well-meaning grandparent or teacher who was holding on desperately to the fine and corset-bound traditions of Victorian/military/religious England. The body can and does carry highly dysfunctional attitudes of posture and styles of movement, long after the original influence has disappeared from the person's life.

This lifted sitting position - which I call Edge-of the-seat Syndrome (EOSS) - creates ENORMOUS levels of excessive tension in the low and mid back and neck and..... well everywhere really. Also, it is a position that once adopted, disallows and discourages (yes, you've guessed it!) natural diaphragm breathing. EOSS is commonly seen in very busy people - mums of young children, nurses and the like. People who are SO busy, that when they sit down they never REALLY sit down fully, as within a fraction of a microsecond they'll be called upon to get on their feet again!

It's also a common pattern in those who may term themselves "lazy". Brought up a in a family with an overzealous work ethic, or influenced by a Superparent who would only ever allow themselves to be stopped by a terminal dose of Bubonic Plague, these people may, in the presence of ANY level of relaxation in their bodies, be instantly haunted by a very real feeling of impending punishment or criticism.

Structurally, EOSS creates a situation where the skeleton is not being properly utilised as a weight-bearing system. When sitting in this position, the EOSS sufferer bears their weight primarily on the back of their legs - the hamstring muscles - with an ever-so-slight forward lean. Dropping back a bit, and committing their weight into the base of the pelvis creates and allows a greater level of relaxation through the whole of the body. This often feels like a 'slouch' to the EOSS sufferer. The straight-edge test will prove this not to be the case.

The other progenitor of EOSS is of course, a history of low back pain that creates discomfort as soon as a settled sitting position is adopted. You can probably appreciate that this may become a vicious circle as the years go by if the back pain issue is not resolved.

I remember one client a few years ago, who'd had severe back pain every day for the last sixteen years. She was a classic EOSS case. Ballet trained, and on show all day as a cabin crew member for an international airline. Very well presented - but HUGELY lifted up in her posture. She booked in with me but was very late for her appointment. I only got chance to have a quick chat with her but pointed out my observations and encouraged her to commit her weight to her bones whilst standing and sitting. I never saw her again but got a message about a month later telling me that she hadn't had a scrap of back pain since that day...

## EXERCISE 05- SITTING IN YOUR SITTING BONES

Try this.

Sit on a high surface, like a worktop, with your legs dangling over the side. Bring your attention to your spine.

'Sit up' as much as you can, pulling your lower back into a hollow. Notice how your upper body is pitched forward of an imaginary centreline, and the contact of your body on the worktop is transferred away from your pelvis, and much more on to the backs of your thighs - this is the position adopted by those suffering from Edge Of the Seat Syndrome.

Now 'slump' as much as you can, so that your low back pushes backwards. Notice how your pelvis also collapses backwards, putting the body contact on to your tailbone, and and how your head juts forward of the centreline.

Somewhere in the middle of these two extremes is a 'neutral' position. In this position, the head will be above the shoulder, which will be above the hip - all three a nice vertical line. In this position, you should be able to feel the presence of your *ischial tuberosities* - the 'sitting bones' at the base of your pelvis - contacting the worktop. They are termed 'sitting bones' as they are perfectly designed to be the point of contact whilst sitting. Once you have contacted the SBs with your awareness, begin to settle more of your body weight directly into these bony supports (taking care to disallow any tipping back of the pelvis which would create a 'slump'). Then refer to *EXERCISE 04 - Still Standing Practice* - and begin to carefully examine your body from this perspective.

This sitting position is a 'middle ground' as it were. Neither too 'up' nor too 'down'. Ideally the lumbar spine is close to vertical. Ask somebody to check your low back with a straight-edge. In this position it is eminently possible to breathe using your diaphragmatic breathing method.

This position takes a little training. Most people's muscles are not set up for this position as a default. The best training method is to actively attempt to FEEL your SBs contacting the chair seat's surface every time you sit down. Once this has become familiar, make this sitting a PRACTICE, by setting up your position in a simple and firm chair, and then spending ten minutes attempting to commit your body weight ever more deeply to your SBs. Learn to sit in your skeleton. A vertical commitment of your sitting frame to the gravitational vector will eventually result in a gentle upthrust throughout your spine, supporting all of the attached muscles and other structures in the optimum way.

One more thing. Sticky *Post-It* notes. Best invention ever. Get some. Write things on them like...

BREATHE OUT
FEET ON FLOOR PLEASE
PERCHING?

...and stick 'em to your computer screen, TV or any other place where you hang out for any length of time and may have the tendency to drift into unconscious postural strangeness.


## Everybody's wonky!

Wonkiness (technical term) is universal. I can't envisage that any-body is in possession of perfect symmetry. Life's just too... well, *knobbly* for that to be the case! When we talk about improving alignment, Improvement is the key word - perfection is not the aim, and attempts to cultivate such a thing as perfection should be avoided at all costs. You'll be setting yourself up for a whole heap of disappointment if you go along that particular road!

So again, alignment should definitely be viewed as a PRACTICE rather than a RESULT. This means bringing AWARENESS to our body positions and habits during everyday activities. By developing verticality through still standing practice, releasing body tension via breathing correction, and paying a gentle attention to ourselves during the daily slog, the fruits of True Alignment will ripen nicely.


## Watching the world go by...

I would also recommend a half-hour's practice, maybe once a month, of sitting on a bench in a busy shopping centre just to watch the world walk by. The more that you get in touch with the quirks of your own body's positioning and movement, the more you'll be drawn to notice the varied and interesting ways that others have developed to propel themselves along.

You'll see a lot of people (probably the greater percentage) *leaning forward* as they walk. This person usually walks fast, and probably walks fast wherever they go. They have the standing-up version of 'Edge of the Seat Syndrome' and their need to arrive on (or before time) or general guilt about being 'lazy' will propel them to walk about twice as fast as the rest. You may see a few people leaning slightly backward as they walk, and are probably 'digging their heels' in to some extent. These people are generally reticent to arrive at their (or any) destination in their lives,.

Some may show a 'dropped' upper body posture. If elderly, they may have been a EOSS sufferer when younger. If younger, they may be tall and teenage and could be finding a swift vertical entry into the adult world a bit much to take on! Then there's the shoulder lifter. The arms seem short and may lack a natural swing as the person walks. This person will be an upper-body breather, the shoulder girdle lifted off the rib cage to create more breathing space in the upper part of the lungs. They may also be a quick walker as they're likely to feel a bit overwrought with all that adrenaline in their system.

Finally, the one in a hundred. This person is vertical, through luck, grace or training and can be spotted a mile off in a crowd. They GLIDE along, and emanate a quiet air of confidence and assured solidity. You'll know what I mean when you see them.

# Relaxation

'Relaxation' seems to me to be a much maligned and misunderstood practice - even the word is used with disdain by many. Upon hearing me utter the the word "relaxation", my clients frequently show an immediate distraction response, swiftly followed by something like...

*"I don't have time to relax. I'm too busy. I have a job and a family as you know and I have a thousand and one things to do at the weekend" (you liberal-minded hippie-like New Age person - get yer 'air cut)*

(I added that last bit by the way) And I never even mentioned the weekend for heaven's sake! Sounds like some folk may equate 'relaxation' with 'laziness' or 'lack of work ethic' or see it as some sort of luxury that they can ill afford. However the immediacy of their response and "Hrumph!"-like retort suggests to me that they are **DESPERATE** to partake in this most noble of pursuits.

So let me set out my thoughts regarding relaxation. I'm convinced that many people view 'relaxation' as a psychological phenomenon, or 'being relaxed' as an aspect of character. For now, I'm going to apply the term 'relaxation' purely to the **structure** of the body, specifically directed toward the muscular system Etymologically, the word "relax" when broken up into "re-" and "lax" suggests that something goes *towards looseness* **again.** So it must have at one stage been loose, became tighter and is now in looseness again.

I love to muse on 'Universal Truths' - things that are true throughout the whole of existence and applying to everybody - you know, death, and income tax, stuff like that. One of those truths, is that every system in the Universe is in a constant state of contraction and expansion. Some contractions and expansions are very small, rapid and easy to observe - the breath of a hamster for example. We see expansion and contraction playing out in the wider environment as the seasons pass from winter through summer and back again. Even apparently immovable lumps such as mountains, and big swooshy things like galaxies are subject to the same kind of cyclic change, but over a much greater period of tIme. Change is constant. Things grow, things fall. Stuff gets bigger, stuff gets smaller. Breathe in, breathe out. Expansion, contraction.

Muscle tissue in the body is a contractile substance. It consists of longitudinal fibres that move toward and past each other in bundles to effectively shorten and thicken the whole muscle. Each muscle is attached to a couple of bones by way of tough tendons across a skeletal joint. The contraction of the muscle causes the flexion of the joint and with many joints acting *in concert,* the human frame ambles gracefully across the stage of life.

Muscles work in opposing pairs - flexors and extensors - biceps and triceps in the upper arm for example. As the bicep contracts and the elbow joint flexes, the tricep has to *extend,* and elongate. As we then open the elbow joint, the bicep releases its contraction and re-laxes, and as the tricep goes into contraction, the bicep then elongates beyond its resting length. What makes a strong and effective muscle is its ability to contract efficiently, re-lax quickly, and also to extend and then return to resting length with ease. A good muscle has effective *elasticity.*

## Elasticity

Change is constant. Things get bigger (before they get smaller again). As things get bigger, their elasticity is tested. If their elasticity is not up to the job they will snap or pop (but not crackle [sorry showing me ongoing fondness for a boyhood breakfast cereal there a bit]).

The cultivation of elasticity in the body tissues through intelligent movement is one of the most valuable things that we can do to support ourselves in an ease-ful journey through life. We will discuss this later.

Things are always changing. Things are always moving. Left, right, left, right, turn. Up, down, day, night, vertical, horizontal. In the body, each step of the way through our lives is accompanied by a million contractions and expansions in muscles, joints, vessels and organs. The elasticity of those tissues is the factor that decides whether we flex effectively or break. The muscles are the most actively contractile of all of the body tissues, so it is the muscles that draw my interest most keenly.

## Trauma & Compensation

As a bodyworker, knowing which bits to press and prod is the least part of the job. We actually major as detectives! What is it about THIS person at THIS time in their lives that is bringing about the body discomfort that they present for investigation. The job of a bodyworker is to take as full a history as possible, so that the story behind the presenting complaint can be understood in as broad a context as possible.

The human body is a walking history book. I take the view that EVERYONE is traumatised to some degree. We have all had falls. Some have had broken bones. Many have experienced surgery. Almost everyone has been though periods of emotional stress at some time during their life. We have all had shocks. These events, or periods of difficulty have all left their imprints on our bodies. During trauma, muscles will become tighter, either locally or throughout the system. After the trauma, there will either be a complete return to normal function and healthy elasticity within the soft tissues, or a snag will remain. These snags, (areas of muscular spasm), will bring about compensations in areas other than that of the initial trauma. This may, over time, lead to further compensation, as the mechanical linkages of the body try to find the 'best way out' in the absence of a full healing of the initial trauma site.

When people come along for help, it may be that the pain that they are bringing along has developed quite suddenly, with no obvious cause. One can be sure, in this case, that an older injury is to blame for the presenting problem - an injury which may have occurred some while ago: years, or even decades. On examination of the whole body, there may be obvious restrictions associated with old injury areas that currently have no symptoms. During treatment, as newer symptoms relieve, these old injury sites may flare up briefly. This is a good indication that a recovery process is underway.

## Unconscious Muscular Activity & Clenching

The more subtle part of the detective work is to observe the subtle muscular habits displayed by those who come for help. Postural issues such as leg-crossing whilst sitting are quite obvious to spot. Spotting the much more subtle (but not the less harmful) clenching of the jaw needs a keener level of observation.

Many are prone to muscular activity that is completely unconscious to them. These long-term habits become 'part of the furniture' so to speak and therefore go unnoticed by the person. The habits often start with the *clenching of* various muscles. The parts of the body that are most liable to clenching are the eyes, the jaw and tongue, the hands, the abdomen, the buttocks, the anus, pelvic floor, and the feet. There are many causes of such effects, and a few of these are described below.

Jaw clenching obviously keeps the mouth closed. This stops things going in, and prevents things coming out. Food goes in the mouth. A desire to keep food out of the mouth when replete may have developed very early in life, only to be overridden by a guardian eager to keep the baby well-fed. Words come out of the mouth. Any attempt to withhold on the vocal level will stop up the throat (as we have discussed) and may also result in a clenched jaw. 'Holding one's tongue' may also contribute to tension in and around the mouth. Ideally, (when neither talking or eating) the lips should be lightly sealed, and the teeth slightly apart. A relaxed tongue will snugly fill the mouth cavity.

The arms are the agents of giving and receiving, and the hands, the instruments by which we finely tune our environment. Difficulties in this arena may result in a tendency to unconsciously close the hands into an over-flexed position. Clenching of the muscles of the abdomen may arise as much from vanity as from anxiety. 'Holding in' and 'sticking out' various parts of the body to create the culturally acceptable shape will always create a muscular disturbance throughout the whole of the body.

The anus is a site of much activity in young children. As babies we are basically feeding tubes - in one end and out the other. A guardian's reaction to activities at the lower end of the tube, and the hygiene practices that they apply to their child may set up tensions in that area. A child only gains full control of its anal sphincter at around two years old. Any attempt to insist upon complete toilet training before this time may elicit clenching in the buttock muscles in the child: in effect, the child attempts to create a forced and artificial closure of the sphincter using the larger muscles surrounding the anus.

Unnoticed tension in the pelvic floor, affecting the vagina and anus may arise from experiences of unwanted or unpleasant sexual contact. Pelvic floor tension to prevent the initiation of urination may be related to a regimented or prohibitive toilet training. These pelvic clenchings will lead to chronic tension in the upper part, if not the whole of the leg. The clutching of the feet may be an early response to anxiety and uncertainty.

By gently bringing attention to these habits, the musculature throughout the body can be returned to a more optimum state. It's important to be moderate in one's expectations when it comes to breaking body habits. Each habit arose for a very good reason, and usually as a response to difficulty. The clench will contain within it a degree of pent-up energy. On releasing the habit, that energy will start to move, and may be experienced as memories of and feelings around the events that brought the habit into being. To take six months to break a long-term habit is probably a reasonable expectation.

The body never lies. It cannot. It is a creature of instinct. As a bodyworker, I am acutely aware that any area of increased muscular tension within the bodies of those who lie on my table, is the end (or maybe the middle) of a story. If a tight muscle is not related to a repetitive activity or injury, then it represents an unhappiness somewhere in the person's history, recent or ancient.

In some bodies, the build-up of muscular tension is much more global. It is as if the whole body is a little too 'switched on'. I compare this to leaving the TV on standby mode - that little red light in the corner of the room suggests that the box is ready to spring into action at the miniscule flick of a remote control button. People are like this too. They switch off... but not quite all the way - just in case (any moment now - wait for it...) something is unexpectedly demanded of them.

However these patterns of excessive muscular tension emerge, they can always be changed for the better. The muscles need skilled intervention, and the person under whose ownership they fall needs education in the care of the elastic suit that is their creative springboard for this life. Ultimately, the muscles will demand our attention to keep them, and us, well. We either offer it willingly, via the practices of conscious movement and the stillness of meditation, or they will bring themselves to our awareness through inelasticity and pain.

## Chronic Tension Revisited

We discussed earlier the importance of body alignment in determining the level of chronic tension in the deep postural muscles. However, the onset of a great deal of the tension that we hold within our bodies has more to do with how we *feel*, rather than what we *do* - in other words, how we *respond* both *mentally and emotionally* to the events and happenings that life brings to our door on a day to day basis. When the letter from the bank manager drops through the letterbox, do we tighten up? Or not...?

In the good old days, all we had to worry about was chasing the odd woolly mammoth across the plain, catching it, despatching it, and dragging it back to the cave. If we couldn't manage any of the above, then that (as they say) would be that - nothing else to worry about from that point onward! You certainly knew where you stood back then!

There was a certain physiological harmony offered by such a basic scenario - hunger bringing about a drive to activity, a flood of adrenaline to do the job - kill or flee (depending on the beast), ending with a discharge of accumulated chase energy, whilst digesting a supersize mammoth-burger meal. Then a good sleep and off we go again. We have very little call for the intelligent physiology of the hunt these days - everything captive and already clingfilmed into submission under one convenient supermarket roof - but our radar still goes 'ping' when we sense a threat. In modern times this is not usually a threat to our physical body it has to be said - I ain't seen a charging rhino-saurus in rural Derbyshire for... ooo at least six months.

Because modern domesticated life generally sustains our biology on the level of warmth, shelter and nutrition pretty adequately (on the most part), we have displaced our sense of 'what's threatening' on to matters that may affect our lifestyle and identity, and on to slights aimed at our personality by others. The threat of redundancy or loss

---

of livelihood is a constant worry for many, raising adrenaline and announcing to the body... "ALERT ALERT - CHARGING RHINO INCOMING!". Problem is, no rhino in sight. A wayward comment from an acquaintance that suggests we may be lacking in certain desirable personality traits (pick anything you like here) or second-hand remark from an employer that puts our performance at work into question may have a similar effect upon our internal red alert system. Again, no obvious threat on the horizon but HUGELY raised levels of adrenaline and fight/flight style body tension.

Constantly on red alert, but with no beast to chase or kill and therefore no discharge of pent-up energy, it's no wonder that most of us are wandering around with so much internal tension that we're ready to go KAPOW! at the slightest hint of a minor breach of the Highway Code by another road user. In our 24/7 society that seems to have mislaid the 'pause' button, investing in the practice of the Art of re-laxation has never been more worthwhile.

Chronic body tension decreases the ability of the structures within the body to expand to an adequate level, and consequently the whole expansion/contraction dynamic throughout the system becomes diminished. It is the contraction and expansion of the space within the organism that allows for pumping of vital fluids, whether it be blood, lymphatic fluid, cerebrospinal fluid, digestive or excretory content. Optimum health of the body relies on adequate FLOW of all of these components.

If the contraction/expansion facility of the body becomes diminished, the signature of life itself - FLOW - becomes less than it could be. The fluid transport diminishes, encouraging deposition and furryness on the inside. The consequences to the heart, brain and other organs are all too often evident when our health takes a drastic (and often sudden) turn for the worse. As we've said somewhere above, it's a bit of a shame that the body copes so well with, and compensates so effectively for a detrimental change to its internal environment. When the big one comes, it's like the fuse box blowing in the house - no warning, then all the lights go out.

Remember this one?

> "I just picked up my toothbrush, and my back went on me!
> How can that happen...?"

Well, it happened because it was *ready* to happen. The old 'straw that broke the camel's back' strikes yet again.

Our bodies are so remarkable that they are able to cope with stress, tension and blockage until the very last moment. Maybe, one might think, that if the body was harbouring that much intelligence it would be constantly giving us feedback about the state of play, and guiding us toward making the necessary minor adjustments to avert the major crisis. Silly body! Why didn't it alert us earlier to the upcoming disaster.

Hang on....maybe it did but were we maybe just a little bit distracted at the time?

## The Still, Small Voice

Our bodies are constantly offering us information. Time to eat. What to eat. Time to sleep. Time to get going. Time to get stopping. Time to stop stopping and get going. Put a sweater on. Take your clothes off. Time to drink. Time to say yes. Time to say nay. Time to run away. This is the voice of *Unravelling*, translated into simple, easy to use, bite size instructions for the benefit of human brains. The information is given *in the moment that it is necessary*, and only repeats itself if ignored.

This information that the body provides is quite subtle, and there are three primary obstacles that get In the way of us picking up on its dulcet tones. The first one is body tension. A tight body eventually turns into a numb body, leaving those subtle messages on the far side of a wall of absence of sensation. The second problem is that our attention is elsewhere - either 'out there' beyond our skin, or drawn away from the subtlety of bodily information by the constant chatter and blather created within our mental sphere of activity - the mighty monologue of the brain playing out 24/7 within the great amphitheatre of the cranium!

But the big one, is a tendency to WILFULLY OVERRIDE the advice that is coming to us via the still, small, voice.

*"Look, I'm really tired but...OK.. I'll do it if it'll make you happy..."*

The Art of Relaxation develops from the skill of paying attention, combined with the practise of LISTENING and responding in a smart way to that which we hear. Paying attention is a learned skill that demands time, and space for practice - things that are usually at a premium in the modern busy world.

Many people tell me that they are 'pretty useless at relaxing', but freely admit that they never put any time or effort in that direction! And those who say such things, as I alluded to earlier, may well believe that RELAXATION equates to DOING NOTHING, which could not be further from the truth. It's eminently possible to build a house or conquer the Universe in a relaxed way! Conversely it's possible to lie next to the pool on a sun lounger for a whole week in a body riddled with tension.

So, I would define a relaxed body as being in a state of (what I call) FUNCTIONAL MUSCULAR TENSION - not a complete absence of tension. I like to compare the human body to a string on a musical instrument. Too much tension and the string snaps, but if there is too little tension - well then the string becomes unable to fulfil its potential and produce the note that it is designed for and capable of.

A muscular system that is optimally TONED (which can be the case where there is good alignment) and where there is sufficient elasticity in the muscles, will be a pleasure to live in, and is always a joy to behold either in static form or during movement. The person will show an easiness of gait, and a buoyancy whilst moving through space. As an accompaniment, they may also be possessed of a calm disposition, and will show accurate and appropriate emotional responses. I am convinced from the evidence that I have gleaned from my time in practice, that the body structure that contains 'just the right amount of tension' will reflect extremely positively in the person's mental and emotional realms. More on that later.

So, the cultivation of Functional Tension has many benefits, whereas the build-up of chronic excessive body tension is hugely detrimental on many levels. Functional Tension is optimised through improved body alignment with relation to the gravitational field - in other words, it's something that we develop when we are truly vertical - standing or sitting. The complete RELEASE of body tension (the horizontal effect!) is also hugely important to create muscles that are capable of effective re-laxation,

Vertical, horizontal. Vertical, horizontal. Vertical horizontal. Day after day. Night after night. And so it goes. Anyone who's tried to stay on their feet for more than a couple of days without rest will attest to the difficulty of the task. The muscular structure needs regular release gained through horizontality and sleep. If this isn't attained, it will become more and more fatigued until it is unable to carry out its function as an effector of locomotion and co-ordination. So the practice of horizontal, 'letting go completely' sort of relaxation is also something worth doing (in a 'non-doing' sort of way of course). I like to remind my body of natural, diaphragmatic breathing lying in bed just before sleep, and then to check through my various limbs and appendages for any unwanted tension from the day's toil, releasing it to gravity along with the outbreath.

Much of the sensation associated with undesirable and unhelpful tension within our deep muscular system is *very* subtle, and sits below the level of the radar of our everyday awareness. The tension that we hold at this level becomes so familiar to us that it ends up like that wallpaper that we put up twenty years ago that everyone who visits cringes at... definitely there, insidiously damaging to our health (or street cred), but generally unnoticed during the day to day. It is because of the *subconscious* nature of this deep tension that we need a *practice* to bring it into awareness for a possibility of release.

Some may only ever begin to release these deeper and unnoticed levels of tension on the annual holiday (most of the first week of which is spent being ill as their body of-floads and goes through a significant detoxification). If we choose to neglect to make relaxation a regular, and wilful practice, there's a good chance that we will be forced into submission by an acute back strain or other short-term illness - this is the intelligence of *Unravelling*, working through our body and taking charge of the situation. To bring relaxation practice into conscious regularity is one of the finest things that we can offer ourselves toward the promotion of our own well-being.

# Movement

We could argue that movement is synonymous with life. Even in a sleeping and externally motionless body, the interior seethes with constant movement. The breath is in motion, the blood is in motion, the digestive contents, lymph and excretory fluids are in motion. There is motion along the neurons of the nervous system, and in the mythical and monster-populated landscape that hosts our nightly dreams. When these internal motions cease to be, 'life' as we would categorise it has left the body, but that stillness is to last but for a brief moment before other processes and species are mobilised by the unstoppable tidal swell of *Unravelling*, drawing things ever onward toward another destination for our discarded flesh and bone.

The individualised patterns of muscular arrangement which surround our skeletons, characterise our movement as uniquely as our faces tell us apart. This is why it's easy to recognise my friend's walk from a distance, long before I can make out his facial features. Our movements are highly habituated and conditioned, and are difficult to override without the kind of training that an actor may undergo. Movement styles, postures and gestures are very often copied by children from their guardians and siblings as they grow within a family unit. This can often lead to what may sometimes be erroneously labelled as 'inherited' tendencies to back pain problems within families. Much of the gesturing that we undertake is highly unconscious to the gesturer. This is a fascinating field, and the study of body language allows those trained in this skill to accurately 'read' the hidden intentions of their subject. Interesting stuff.

So we can see that a great proportion of our movement as individuals is highly conditioned, arising from patterns of response of which we have little awareness, and often related to underlying emotional states. A grief-stricken person will walk in a very different manner to someone who's brimming with unvented anger. The excited and happy-go-lucky scamp will not be mistaken for a fearful individual even to the untrained eye. Many who have undergone a period of emotional turmoil in their lives may still be carrying the posture of that experience many years after the waters have settled. It is for these reasons, that the study and practice of movement has such an enormous potential to release not only physical, but also emotional and mental patterning from our being. To give an alternative is to create a situation whereby the individual may become 'unstuck' from a deeply conditioned and unhelpful pattern that they are not even aware of.

If life and movement are inseparable qualities, then to bring awareness to our movement will inform us deeply about our life. Cultivating *conscious* movement, and caring for those structures of our body that are involved in movement is of the utmost importance in our journey of self-awareness. It is the muscles and joints that facilitate the movement of our frame through space. We have talked much of muscles. Let's turn our attention to the joints.


## Range of Motion

In Chinese martial arts teachings, the joints of the body are said to resemble 'pearls on a string.' The task of the joints is to conduct the forces which are induced by body motion effectively through the whole body structure. Ideally, these forces will travel through the exact centre of each joint, as does the string on a pearl necklace, thereby maximising strength, optimising efficiency, and promoting health and longevity for that joint. Misalignment, or excessive tension around the joint will bring the cartilage-lined bone surfaces into an unusual and unhelpful orientation, setting the seed for arthritic changes.

If you ever get a chance to visit a *Cirque de Soleil* show, go see! I love to be reminded of the awesome movement potential inherent within the human body. Watching the performers, I am also saddened by how little of the human being's extensive movement ability is utilised during day to day activities. Each joint has a range of motion. The shoulder complex, for example, is capable of an extraordinary range of directions and fancy twists and turns. The hip joint, which requires greater stability (due to its load-bearing requirements) than the shoulder, is consequently endowed with a lesser, although still impressive, range of motion. The wrist is subtly twisty, and when combined with the accurate hinges of the four fingers and the curly snake-like ability of the thumb, provides us with mind-boggling dexterity.

As an aside, it always makes me chuckle when I watch a sci-fi film where the aliens turn up brandishing 'ultimately superior technology' which has allowed them to travel across the galaxy in their super-stealth spaceship in the blink of an eye, only for us to discover (when they show themselves at the end of the film) that they have hands resembling hedge clippers or half a packet of spaghetti! Perhaps they have other species at home to do the soldering and screw the nuts on to the bolts.

The stalwart hinges of the knee and ankle allow the smaller joints found within the body of the foot to sense, and then accommodate accurately to the ever-changing topography of the floor on which they walk. The small joints in the foot also allow an effective level of shock- absorbency to the rest of the body.

It is in the *axial* skeleton - in the spine and the rib cage - that we find the tiny joints that allow accurate posture and balance to be maintained, and which allow the mechanics of breathing to carry on unhindered during the act of walking, crawling, jumping up and down and whatever other shenanigans we may get up (or down) to.

Much of the movement executed by today's average urban warrior is extremely 'front-centric' (I'm sure that's not a word). In other words, we do an awful lot of stuff in front of our body. Driving, computing, drinking tea - all of these things demand a fairly similar range of motion of the joints. To take our joints though a more complete range of movement (and I absolutely recommend this) we usually need to get involved in a sport.

Some sports are very repetitive in their movements but have obvious health benefits for the musculoskeletal and cardiovascular systems. However, it is the kinds of leisure activities that have developed body movement as both a science and an artform that have done most to deepen people's appreciation of their movement ability. Dance, martial arts, yoga, tai chi, and other exotic movement forms have done much to improve the health and promote the longevity of an ever increasing number of people who have become practitioners of these disciplines over the last forty years or so. Keep it up.

## Growing older

In my practice, I have had the privilege to assist people from many different walks of life with their body conundrums. It has been fascinating to work with many different age groups. I am astounded by the occasional eighty five year old who still regularly breezes a nine-day trek in Nepal. These people are few and far between, but the secret of their success is in their attitude towards body movement. The three key words are MEASURED, CONSCIOUS and REGULAR. They are life's true athletes. They may have never run the hundred metres or swum the English Channel, but their attitude toward their body movement practices has always contained a great deal of consciousness.

The body does change as we get older, there's no doubt about that. Levels of hydration and elasticity in the tissues is far less in our eighth decade than in our second, but REGULAR movement gives us our best chance of maintaining our inherent bounciness. The joints and associated structures operate on a 'use it or lose it' basis, so it makes sense to develop a daily routine whereby the joints are systematically taken through their range of motion. This can be done standing, simply working each joint through its range. Fingers, elbows, shoulders, shoulder blades, jaw, hips, knees, ankles and toes (standing on one leg whilst working the joint). The spine can be mobilised through slow swinging rotations to either side. This stuff is so simple and has untold benefits right now, and increasingly so as we enter our later years.

I have many clients who say that they cannot touch their toes any more, but the worrying thing is that they are not sure for how long they have not been able to touch their toes! The loss of the ability to spread the thumb away from the hand is common in the elderly. This can have devastating consequences, but could be quite easily prevented. If you are forty years old and can do this movement quite easily, then do the movement deliberately, as an exercise, three times each day. In this way, the day will never arrive when you are unable to do it. Simple.

In my experience, those who develop a tendency to fall later in life are invariably carrying excessive tension in their legs and feet. As far as I can see, it is the *foot* that is the primary organ of balance in the body. Its complexity senses the changing terrain as we walk, accommodating and informing the structures above. When we have tight feet, the attempt to balance whilst walking is taken on by other joints, further up in the body, which are inherently unsuitable for the job. Taking the joints of the feet through their ranges, standing practice, self-massage, meditative walking, reflexology and employing the use of a foot spa, are all useful ways to keep the feet soft, conscious and responsive.

I believe that the knee is the most crucial joint in the whole of the skeleton. When we cease to use our knees to lower and raise the body, we will start to bend with our back. The knees respond unfavourably to this compensation and start to become, and feel less reliable. When people tell me that they can't bend to get into the cupboard under the sink very well any more, I know for sure that they stopped using their knees to lower the body probably about twenty years ago. Overuse of the back for bending will eventually tighten the muscles of the back, and also the back of the pelvis and hips. This is when descending stairs starts to become difficult. The person inevitably then feels less safe and begins to tighten their legs and feet in an attempt to create more safety, but this only makes things worse. A near miss or an actual fall when coming down the stairs sets the seeds for finally destroying the person's confidence in their own support system, extinguishing their desire to move around freely, thus diminishing their vitality. So in the light of this: if you are forty and you can still do a standing squat, do it three times, twice a day for the rest of your life. You could save yourself from half a lifetime of misery.

It could be argued that the spine is the most crucial composite structure in the body. The joints and deep muscles of the spine are teeny tiny, but are responsible for our fine adjustment of movement and have an important role in effective co-ordination of body and limb. These muscles are the first to suffer from the effects of stress, and excessive tension here will have an insidious and highly deleterious effect on our well-being. This tension may go unnoticed for a long while, as the person's *exterior* musculature may be relatively elastic, betraying an interior that is becoming increasingly uneasy. To bring awareness to, and to mobilise the joints of the spine, by employing movements that are small-ish, rhythmic and rotatory, or spiralic has to be one of the most health-promoting activities of all time. Swimming probably does it, Pilates and yoga get you in there to some extent. The movements of the Chinese systems - Qi Gong, Tai Chi - definitely. I reckon that the ultimate way in is the internal Chinese martial system of circle-walking - Ba Gua Zhang.

If you look after the core, then the periphery will sort itself out. If you care for the bottom, the top end will pretty much look after itself. Pay attention to the base. Take good care of the roots. Enjoy the flowers and the fruit.

## Spontaneous Movement

When was the last time that you moved your body in a way which was just what you fancied doing in the moment that you fancied doing it? Can you remember the last time?

Unlike the majority of adults, little children do it all the time. When in the supermarket aisle, they don't think to themselves...
*"Hmm, I've just noticed an inner urge to go WOOWOOWOOWOO, jump up and down and wave my arms in the air- but s'pose I best curb my desire because it'll look a bit weird..."*
Of course not.

So at what age did <u>you</u> cease to follow that urge to movement, either with your body or with your voice? Have a think for a moment... here's some music.

I am proud to say that I still do the uncensored version of the WOOWOOWOOWOO thing in the privacy of my own home. It's GREAT... and I really encourage you to do the same. I have done it in the great outdoors also. I specifically make a pilgrimage to the top of Mount Snowdon once a year out of the tourist season to perform an extended version. I have been known to do such things in a field close to my home, and fortunately have only surprised an innocent dog-walker on the one occasion. I also momentarily forgot where I was one day and did something a bit like a bark by the cheese counter in Sainsbury's.

I really hope that I'm not alone on this one, and that you also partake regularly in this marvellous and health-promoting activity. If not, do give it a go sometime.

Of course, the containment and wilful restriction of movement and speech is important... but not all of the time. To outpour is a natural tendency, and to deprive ourselves of that opportunity, whether on a physical or vocal level, can be highly damaging to our well-being. As with relaxation practice, to give this tendency a regular outing does nothing but good. If we can cultivate this kind of *ideomotion*, where the impulse of our internal world is immediately translated into movement or speech, we will be far less likely to *override* the still, small voice when it offers guidance for our good.

# EMOTION

I think that it's really important not to get too emotional when talking about the emotions. All that shouting and wailing - most uncivilised. But hang on... is that what emotions are about - an emotional *display* ? Surely the fundamental nature of what we experience as emotionality must be something a little more er... fundamental - more basic, and... well...I have to say it - a bit more useful! Now don't think that I'm a cold fish or anything like that. I can blub with the best of them and I do get a bit overexcited at times, but I have to say that shouting at our puppy when she's sinking her playful teeth into my toes is something that I'm having to practice hard at - it doesn't come naturally to me.

I have always made an assumption that *every* aspect of the Human System has a usefulness that is related in some way to survival of the individual. This must be true for emotions also. Let's see.

If I were a single-celled organism (and I may well be one, who's having a rather bad dream), then my basic needs are for

- the right temperature in which to exist
- the correct level of moisture to remain squidgy, and
- the right kind of nutrition.

...and... nope. That's about it really.

In this current incarnation as a human being type of organism, I may try to convince myself that my needs are to drive a particular model of fast red car and eat only Big Macs, but my *basic* needs are pretty much identical to those of a *Paramecium*\*\* If I'm cold I'll move towards getting warmer. If I'm dry I'll look for a drink. If I'm hungry I'll eat anything that's got fuel in it. If you're reading this book right now (which it looks from here like you are) then it's a sure-fire bet that <u>your</u> particular basic needs for warmth, hydration and nutrition are being adequately and continually met. If they weren't, you wouldn't be wasting your time reading - you'd be out there trying to get fed and watered. It's only the adequate satisfaction of those basic needs that allows the notion of *choices* - between blue car and red car, Big Mac or Quarter Pounder - to

---

\*\* *Pa-rer-mees-eeum* - a microscopic and wiggly pond-dwelling thingy.

arise in the first place. The tendency of choices to masquerade as needs puts us way out of touch with the basic nature of our emotional mechanisms.

Although my "needs" as a cosmopolitan being are apparently complex, my real needs are simple and basic, *and are driven by the primeval needs of the individual cells of my body.* My basic emotions are the same as those of my wiggly microscopic cousin - they serve at the very fundamental level to **reorient** me in relation to my environment.

# Strategies of Orientation

Let's look at this in a bit more detail. Did you ever watch *Question of Sport* on the TV? There was a bit called *What Happened Next?* They'd show a clip of some famous sporting event, and freeze-frame it just at the point at which some unexpected something occurred. You know like the guy's just about to take a shot at goal in the World Cup Final and a piano falls unexpectedly out of the sky, lands on top of him and changes the course of history forever. So the film stops and the panel are asked... well the clue's in the title really.

So then. Here's me, sitting on a park bench on a beautiful hot summer day, watching the world go by. I'm sitting still, and the world's going by. Now, here's four scenarios which we'll freeze frame so that you can play along.

1) A rhinoceros comes into view, hurtling toward my park bench at a rate of knots.

2) An ice cream van appears over the other side of the park, and slowly trundles across my line of vision, and heads into the distance.

3) A lithe, bronzed roller skater glides up to the bench and hitches her glistening leg up on to the seat beside me to adjust her skate.

4) A bee lands on my face and proceeds to stick it's stinger into the end of my nose.

Four scenarios which involve me in the centre being still, and then a change in my environment, perceived by my senses - in this case, something *coming into view*. So viewers, lets play *What Happened Next?*

Well, the next thing that happens is an *internal response* in relation to my perception. Something comes into view, and I have a response:

- firstly on the hormonal level (say, adrenaline)
- secondly on the mental level (decision)
- thirdly on the neurological level (fire up the engines)
- and finally on the muscular level (action).

I *sense* the event, my internal system gauges the *need* around that perception, a *decision* is made, I *gather* myself into a response, and I *act*. My basic actions in relation to any presenting scenario will fall into only a few categories, and will be no different to those of cousin *Paramecium* (we don't see that side of the family much - not fond of ponds).

My actions will be either...

1) MOVE MYSELF *AWAY*
Run like hell!!

2) *FOLLOW* PERCEIVED OBJECT
Give chase

3) *PULL* PERCEIVED OBJECT *TOWARDS* ME
Well hello there....

4) *PUSH* PERCEIVED OBJECT *AWAY*
Get this thing away from me!

The above responses may be a little semi-autobiographical (ahem), and each individual would of course have their own peculiar and particular way of responding, but the actual *styles of orientation* are very few, and are related to fulfilment of the very basic needs of the organism in relation to its continuing survival - Run, feed, mate, fight.

In essence, we either, move ourselves away, move toward, draw in towards us, push away, or choose to do nothing. In the four scenarios described earlier, we would probably label the responses of the person on the park bench as being "emotional" in their nature, but in the light of the above, I would like to posit 'emotion' as being primarily a *physiological* phenomenon, rather than any kind of *psychological* issue, and in doing so, have a look at the *anatomy* of emotion and its relation to the physical body. If we entertain the possibility that the emotional component of our being has a simple, and recognisable anatomy, then this anatomy (just as we have seen with regard to the *physical* structure of the body) will be *organised* to a greater or a lesser degree. *Improved* organisation of our emotional anatomy should lead to improved functioning.


## Emotion and 'Emotionality'

We have discussed previously how the lives of many are blighted by pain in the physical body. The more 'invisible' (but none the less real) scourge of 'emotional pain' is probably cited by a far greater number of people as being the greatest obstacle in the way of the fulfilment of their true potential.

The lives of many people are blighted by pain in the physical body. The more 'invisible' (but none the less real) scourge of 'emotional pain' is cited by just as many as being the greatest hindrance to their happiness.

When people talk in desperation about their 'emotional pain' and the dreadful effect that it has on their lives, they may be talking about very real sensations of discomfort that arise from chronic tension in their bodies which can be directly attributed to some ongoing issue - maybe the loss of a dear one, or the frustration of having to deal with an intractable dilemma. They may however, be making reference to the difficulties that they encounter with a tendency toward uncontrollable, unpredictable and wayward *emotional display,* whose very visibility to others in their world brings about huge difficulty in relationships, the workplace, or in social situations. Emotional display is very normal. We cry, we shout, we shake, we laugh. All of these things are a natural response to the experience of events in our world. But when our responses are uncontrollable, exaggerated, and particularly when they are 'inappropriate' for the situation at hand, then we may suffer from this display having a detrimental effect on our opportunities to interact socially with others, in a fruitful way.

If the emotional component of our physiology is in good order, and is consequently demonstrating a high level of organisation and function, our responses will **always** be effective in creating for us an appropriate orientation in the face of the constant shift of circumstance in our world.

My feelings are that when the emotional mechanisms of our physiology are in good order, and are showing a highly developed level of organisation, our responses are **always** effective in creating an appropriate orientation of our organism toward the constant shift of events in our world.

So let's have a look at the four **strategies of orientation.**

# FEAR
## - the strategy of MOVING AWAY

Fear is our number one self-preservation strategy. We remove ourselves from the presenting danger. If this one wasn't in primary position, then we would not be around for long to do anything more complex! This strategy is geared toward FLIGHT away from a perceived danger (such as a charging rhino), it is a high energy strategy and primarily involves the legs, back of the pelvis and hips, and the front of the lower spine in its execution.

# AVERSION/ANGER
## - the strategy of PUSHING AWAY

This strategy comes in second. If the flight has failed and the source of danger is encroaching into our personal space, we fight. This strategy is also high energy and involves pushing, and so is in the domain of the back of the arms and the upper back, and an anchoring of the body through the front of the feet.

# ATTACHMENT/LONGING
## - the strategy of FOLLOWING

When we are safe, then we can feed and mate. Without safety we can do neither. In feeling safe we can look out into our world for those things that will nourish us and promote our continuing existence. The energy of this strategy is much more leisurely. It also involves the legs, but in a much less adrenaline-fuelled way. It has a more steadfast and determined quality - the long haul as opposed to the mad dash. We know that we need what we need and are determined to follow it until it arrives within our space.

# DESIRE
## - the strategy of PULLING TOWARD

On encountering at close quarters the object of our longing, we are in a position to draw it into our space - either into our digestive system, or for mating purposes. This strategy is related to the front of the body, the muscles of the chest and the bicep muscles of of the arms. This strategy envelops the object of desire and holds things dear.

The four strategies of *Moving Away, Pulling Toward, Pushing Away,* and *Following* are BASIC and PRIMAL responses which are geared toward survival of the organism. When freely allowed - when we let our basic instinct lead the way - we can't go far wrong. I've always subscribed to the notion that if we go through life knowing clearly when to say yes to things and when to say no, life should be a doddle.

Cousin *Paramecium* never has a problem with this. He flagellates himself (must have a word with Auntie *Amoeba* about this) toward food and moisture, and away from irritating and noxious influences. He has not been known to swim into an acidic environment just for kicks, and has never been one to keep off the water for a day or so just to see what happens. No, he's a simple guy, with simple needs, and he knows how to get them met. Our whole body is made up of simple, single cells a bit like cousin *Paramecium*. Unfortunately, when they are clumped together into a human body, things start to go a bit awry. In a community of cells, there obviously has to be some sort of teamwork. Cells are no longer free agents, able to move hither and thither without so much as a 'by your leave'. Now, it's the well-being and survival of the whole community that's at stake,

You don't see animals in the wild having a problem with acting on instinct - if they failed to act on instinct they'd have a huge problem but wouldn't be around for very long to contemplate how big a problem they had! So it seems like the individual cells within wild creatures are acting very much like Cousin *Paramecium*, but in a coherent, concerted and organised fashion, offering the four strategies of *Moving Away, Pushing Away, Following,* and *Pulling Toward,* to the whole organism, and giving their very best shot at promoting both their own, and therefore the whole creature's survival. The cells of a more complex multicellular being are still being selfish in their actions, but seem to be aware that in order to survive they have a vested interest in communicating with the whole community of cells within the larger body.

So what is it with good old *homo sapiens?* What is it that gives us such a problem with acting simply by way of our instinct? We've not lost that ability - those calls to one of the four strategies are still operating within our systems during every waking moment of every day - and often they do move us. But we've got into a habit of overriding those calls.

*"Quick!! Run like hell!!"*
"Calm down, calm down... Can't you see I'm in the middle of reading *'Hello!'* magazine? The rhinoceros will just have to wait..."

This just about sums it up. We override our instincts, and eventually diminish our ability to hear the message. Our grasp on the primary reason for our emotional physiological responses becomes lost to us. Our emotions become (very much like the body in our last chapter) a 'bit of a nuisance'. The brain has taken over the asylum.

Having said all that, let us not decry the marvellous neocortex. It is this big modern brain, not shared by other species, that has allowed us to organise ourselves differently - giving us interesting alternatives to purely instinctual responses to events. It is the ability of the developed nervous system to sidestep and override pure instinct, and from there make considered decisions about our actions in the face of events in our outer world, that has propelled us to the heights of creative endeavour, and technological know-how. Our big brains worked out how to provide sustainable warmth, hydration and food, by way of tool making and domestication of crops and animals. We subsequently realised the luxury to consider the world around us in a much more relaxed fashion, sowing the seeds for art, philosophy and technology.

The modern self-reflecting, 'conscious' human mind that we recognise today arose as a side-effect of our ability to override our basic and primal emotional strategies. This overriding itself is a by-product of human domestication - the basis of 'civilization'. However, let's not get all triumphant about this and be tempted to consign our emotions to the same dustbin within which we have carefully stowed our physical bodies - we do that at our peril. The energies that drive the animal within each human are raw and powerful, and underpin our vitality, health, strength and sanity. These forces issue from nature, and connect from our bodies toward our evolving human mind by way of our emotional physiology - those simple strategies of reorientation. Making conscious this pathway between the 'animal and human' within ourselves is a journey well worth taking.

## Emotional Anatomy

Our body is a responsive system. It cannot not respond. We perceive events by way of our senses, our perceptions are weighed up and responses ensue. These responses are initiated by the nervous system and the physical frame delivers the action via the muscular system. Each of the four strategies is, by its very nature, destined to activate the muscular system, and therefore the body's movement, in a different way. We do not run on our hands (very often). The strategy of *moving away* through fear primarily acts to get our legs under us and to get the hell out of wherever we are. *Following* driven by longing also activates the legs, but reaches out with the arms also. When we arrive, our arms are used for *pulling toward* us the object of desire. If it's not quite what we wanted we may then *push away* with a different set of muscles in the arms, averse to our catch.

If all of these primary strategies are working freely and optimally within and through an individual, we should see a balanced development of the muscular system throughout the body. This, however, is unusual, as most individuals are compromised in their ability to spontaneously operate one or more of these four strategies, and may be biased toward a default of only one. This results in an overdevelopment of the musculature in certain portions of the body at the expense of other areas.

## The 'Civilizing' Influence

The expression of instinctual responses via bodily movement is somewhat muted in modern life. The intervention of logic into the human animal's world has created beings who still perceive, still feel the hormonal impetus, and still experience the firing up of the nervous system, but who fail to follow through with the body. Without this overriding and inhibiting tendency we would, of course, never have become domesticated enough to create the kind of human communities that we live in today. The health of our bodies has, however, been the major casualty of this domestication.

Wild animals, on perceiving potentially life-threatening danger from a predator, will respond to the sudden call to flight with an engagement of the whole body, in the action of running away, or by fighting if the predator should catch up. The last-ditch attempt at survival comes via 'freezing' - the creature 'plays dead' in the hope that his attractiveness as a snack will be diminished. If a grazing animal is called to alert by a sudden smell on the wind, but it turns out that there is no actual threat, its body will shiver and tremble for a few seconds before it returns to grazing, as the energy that has been initiated into the nervous system is discharged, leaving the muscular system in a state of relaxed preparedness for the next event.

We see this tremor in humans subsequent to accidents and trauma. The discharging of nervous energy through the muscular system is a perfectly natural process. However, an individual's tendency to habitually block their muscular responses when the nervous system is fired up may prevent this discharge, 'locking in' the energy of response and resulting in a 'traumatised' individual. I have experienced countless examples of clients who, after receiving bodywork, may go through several days of shaking and trembling within their bodies. My belief is that this happens as the nervous system discharges energy that has become lodged within their body, often for many years.

In domesticated animals (of which humans are one species), when the nervous system directs, but the body fails to act, chronic muscular tension is the obvious result. The muscles are contracting, but we ain't goin' nowhere. It's a bit like being in the car and having our foot on the accelerator and the brake at the same time. It's no wonder there's such a strong smell of 'burning clutch' in the air these days...

## Emotion and *Unravelling*

The four emotional strategies are the most simple expression of the ever-present force of *Unravelling*. Their stage directions will *always* lead us down the path of survival and health. When they are acknowledged and consciously included within our inventory of human qualities, they offer us a deep and solid connection with our bodies, and to the Earth beneath our feet. When ignored or even worse, dismissed and sidelined by the habitual intervention of logic and reason, they become wayward and unpredictable, and then call to us loudly through unusual displays and behaviours. The wilful or unwitting act of suppression of these simple strategies creates disturbance in the natural rhythm of the breath, creating pressure, and deep muscular tension within the body. Flows throughout the vessels are disturbed and reduced, bringing about depositation in tubes, and restriction in chambers. No space. No transport. Rubbish piling up in the streets.

## The Cell's Tale

*The inevitable build-up of toxicity within the system eventually showed up deep within the basic fabric of the land. The rivers flowed more slowly, there was a smell in the air. Paramecium's distant cousin, that simple soul, working as he always had for the good of the nation, did the very best he could in the only way he knew how. He went on Moving Away, Pulling Toward, Pushing Away, Following, in concert with his neighbours, and in tune with the seasons and rhythms. Nothing difficult about that. But the guy at the Head of Government was a long way away. He wasn't listening over there in Neocortexia. His concerns were for shiny things, self-promotion, and 'Hello!" magazine.*

*Paramecium's cousin was getting sick, but no-one really noticed. He wasn't on the A-list. He and others like him kept themselves pretty much to themselves, out in the periphery. They* knew how it all worked, but their way of life sounded simple and quaint to the guy at the Head of Government. Surely those who surrounded the guy at the top were just like us? he mused. Why wouldn't they listen?

Paramecium's cousin's family and neighbours were unwell - the water was becoming bad, the food inedible. There was disturbance in the community - bad people, acting out of their own interest, not bothered with family or community cohesion. People just out for themselves. These bad folks no longer looked up at the sky, to the beauty of a leaf in autumn, to a sunset. They never knew nor cared less whether the moon was full or new. They looked up to the guy at the the Head of Government as as an example of how to live their lives. They became greedy, walling themselves off in their little groups. They chattered and distracted, never sitting silently any more, never giving any space to allow the voice of Unravelling - the way of Nature - to issue forth from their hearts.

Paramecium's cousin despaired. What was wrong with these people? They are just like us - they used to be friends and neighbours. How could they have changed so much?

Soon these people were gathering together in communities, barricading themselves in stockades, and sending out scouts during the night to steal the community's food. Their slick philosophy of self-interest had now spawned a well-oiled political machine, and members would make evangelical forays into far-flung communities, attempting to convert those of the 'Old Ways' into disciples of the New Body Order.

There was news of chaos in other regions. Invasions were reported, and interventions by Government agencies to restore order. Things were getting worse. The waters stopped flowing and turned stagnant. The air stank of rot. There were freak storms and strange sudden flashes of radiation in the sky.

Paramecium's cousin and his remaining family and neighbours despaired. Their water was contaminated. their food was sparse. Even the air became caustic. Paramecium's cousin, in a moment of madness even considered defecting, and going over to the New Body Order, simply to get food for his family. But Unravelling was strong in Paramecium's cousin.

He prayed to his ancestors who lived in those times before the development of community - free floating beings who were guided by nature and would let nothing distract them from the pure instinctual way of life. Paramecium's cousin looked up to the stars, and called on the power of Unravelling to heal the land.

And then the next day the lights went out. No-one knew it was coming, and there was no-one left to talk about it afterwards.

---

# AIDS FOR EMOTION

## Bringing Attention to Emotion

To take a step back, in the face of a highly energised emotional display is tricky. When we are raging with anger, destructive to ourselves and those in our immediate environment, it is highly unlikely that we would choose (or have the presence of mind) to stop dead, sit down and FEEL deeply into the energy coursing through our body, observing it like we would any other perceptual event. When we are in the depths of the sobbing that accompanies the experience of our seemingly unending grief, would it be likely that we would choose to hold our awareness slightly differently and FEEL into the sensations of the experience?

A highly charged emotional experience is all too often *overwhelming*, and does not easily allow for an unbiased examination by our awareness. The subtlety of the Impartial Observer is sidelined by the raw energy of a highly emotionally charged event. If we do, however, train ourselves into this way of operating, we will begin the transformation of our destructive emotional displays back into the subtle strategic orientation from which they arose. Each of the strategies is, in its inception, truly tiny. It is the still, small voice, that says 'move away' or 'follow'.

So how is it that the simple orientation strategy of *Moving Away*, for some people, has become demonically transformed into an almost continual experience of outright terror that blights their every waking moment? How has the awesomely destructive power of human rage arisen from that gentle innate strategy that we have for *Pushing Away* that which we wish to exclude from our personal circle? And how can we return these distorted and altered energies back to their simple, natural, and intelligent form? It is probably useful to see these warped and destructive states as *highly magnified* versions of the original simple strategies. They have become that way due to a *disallowing* somewhere along the way - a disallowing that has become a habitual tendency, creating a backlog that disturbs our internal systems on many levels.

If the strategy of *Moving Away* is continually and habitually disallowed, it will eventually result in a diminishment of bodily motion in the face of any kind of danger. The energy necessary to propel the flight process will still be released into the body, but nothing happens - the old brake and accelerator problem again. If this process is repeated often enough, our nervous system will eventually remain in a permanently aroused state, developing within us a pervasive feeling of fear. This continual feeling in our body created by 'blocked' flight may eventually serve to convince us that anything and everything that moves in our visual field is a potential source of danger. We may 'spook' at unexpected events in the outside world, or become paralysed in the face of change. Requests for our participation by others in our world may become impossible to deal with. We may even become petrified at the changes and workings of our own mind as it examines the past and looks toward the future. At worst even the capricious and fleeting sensations in our own body may become for us a perceived source of danger. At this stage there seems no escape from the terror that we experience.

When the nervous system is constantly powered up and no flight is attempted, the breathing mechanism and the muscular system are the first casualties. Chest breathing becomes the norm, and chronic tension in the legs simply adds to the feeling of ungroundedness and instability in the world of the fear-ridden individual. Eventually, the energy of a disallowed strategy always needs to find some way to discharge itself from the system. Tremors, busyness, rapid and continual talking, and panic attacks are the signature symptoms of the terrified.

A second example. When we fail to operate the simple strategy of *Pushing Away*, the world 'out there' will inevitably encroach further and further into our personal space. Our boundaries are breached, the most private aspects of our being are invaded. The energy of the fight is initiated into the nervous system, but again, no action is taken. Long term disallowance of this strategy will, once more, put the nervous system into a state of constant arousal. The person will accumulate chronic tension in the upper back and neck, and show the chest breathing pattern associated with anger. In this case, the discharge of energy may come as sudden outbursts of temper and rage, often initiated by relatively insignificant events. Because the bodily expression of *Pushing Away* has become disallowed, there may be an attempt to push away by other means. The person may develop a 'thundercloud' personality, or have a tendency to use language as a way of keeping the world at a distance.

The strategy of *Following* is a fairly gentle but relentless energy. As we identify that which we need, we orient our body towards our target and begin to move in its general direction. To block this strategy is to short-circuit the possibility of growth and furtherance within our lives. Instead of a joyful rambling toward this and that with an eager and gently forward lean to the body we will continually 'dig our heels in' creating tension in the front of of the leg and abdomen. Because we are thwarting our attempt at exploration we may experience a deep longing and resentment toward the abundance of life.

The strategy of *Pulling Towards* is associated with an attempt to envelop the object of desire, and therefore has an association with feeding and mating. Its energy is slightly less urgent than that of flight or fight, but when disallowed often, and over a long period of time, it may ignite into the raging fire of obsession, lust and greed. The breath pattern of rising desire will again be focussed away from the diaphragm and into the upper part of the lungs but the muscles of the chest and upper arms may be over activated, suppressing the movement of the rib cage, exerting unhelpful pressure on the heart and lungs and resulting in a diminished breath volume. This person may appear to be devoid of breathing and may emit a 'creepy' feeling. The undischarged energy building within the system will again need to find a way out on some level if the simple strategy of *Pulling Toward* is not being regularly allowed. This may result in behaviours involving overindulgence followed by a period of abstention - reckless abandon followed by self-recrimination. If this form of discharge is also disallowed and the energy is internalised it may fuel disturbance and fantasy on the mental level, which becomes the only stage on which the strategy of *Pulling Toward* can be enacted.

## So then, what to do....

When the four simple emotional strategies of orientation have become so deeply distorted through *disallowing*, the process bringing them back to a simple and natural form can be a bit tricky to say the least. At this stage, the disallowed strategy will manifest and reveal itself as *symptoms*. The person is now 'ill' and their attention will understandably be drawn by the discomfort of their symptoms. The appearance of symptoms is of course sensible (good old *Unravelling*). The symptoms have arisen and developed from the habitual blocking of natural emotional response. The symptoms are an accurate symbolic representation of the information that we need to lead us back to a 'freeing up' of that tendency to block. However, at this stage of the game, we will have convinced ourselves, (probably subconsciously) that the historical blocking of our response happened for a valid reason, so why would we wish to alter our approach?

*"Oh come on - EVERYBODY knows that getting angry is a BAD thing, silly!"*

So the 'ill' person now attempts to relieve the uncomfortable symptoms, and in the search for a 'cure' they may become hopelessly enmeshed within a medical system that seeks to relieve those symptoms pharmaceutically, and which has no real expertise in seeking out the root of the problem. When symptoms are *relieved* without *resolution*, the problem can only go deeper. The way I am using the word *symptom*, may seem a little unusual. I am referring here to any 'abnormal' body experience that is indicative of a *compensation for* the blocking of natural, emotional response. Looking at it in this way, symptoms will manifest on *all* of the following levels, and lead toward the formation of *character* as it presents itself in the individual. Effects will be observed with regard to:

- levels of body tension
- habitual patterns of body movement
- alterations of physiological function
- presentation style of speech and choice of vocabulary
- style of response to change in the 'outer world'
- style of response to activities of the 'inner world'
- desires and aversions
- patterns of thought and belief.

When you look at the above list you may say...

> *"well these are all things that go to make up 'who I am'"*

...and you'd be right of course. We all have an individual make-up which displays itself on the levels of body, speech, and mind, and that is SHAPED by these very strategies - particularly by their enforced diminishment and consequent exaggeration.

**In 'good health', when the four strategies of *Moving Away, Pushing Away, Following* and *Pulling Toward* are easily and naturally enacted in response to the unpredictable everyday alterations in our inner and outer world, we will remain calm and centred in the face of change. This will create a relaxed musculature, with a smooth and easy movement style and accurate coordination. The relaxation and verticality in the body will produce an ordered interior, optimising flows and promoting the well-being of all physiological functions. Our speech will be direct and clear, not needing to be in anyway manipulative or coercive. That which we move toward for our well-being, on the level of nutrition and relationship, is likely to be clearly chosen, and will give us a favourable response. Our needs will have a quality of sufficiency, seeking out neither too much nor too little. Our thinking mind will be clear and spacious, and we can thereby employ this faculty in the examination of present-moment detail,**

**and also use it for planning the enactment of a broad vision for our lives. Our mindset will be moderate and tolerant.**

Sounds like a 'healthy' person to me!

But this 'ideal' is not the topic in hand. At this moment I am sitting here paralysed by terror, incensed with rage, racked with unbearable longing, and consumed with lust. What do I do next? How do I release myself from this self-made prison that I have constructed from my habit of disallowing?

Simple......stop the fight and ALLOW.

# Allowing

*"Now hang on there one moment Phil. I don't think that you have any idea of the level of the disturbance that is running riot through my system. You obviously have no comprehension of the pressure that has built up in here. If I were to let go and allow, it'd end up all over the walls! - and I'd be apprehended by the local constabulary within the week!"*

OK, so what <u>can</u> you allow to make a start? How about allowing the fact that you're in a bit of a predicament, and that there's a possibility of a way out?

*"Now.... well OK. That doesn't sound so bad. So I don't 'allow' my crazy behaviour and mad speech to be unleashed upon an unsuspecting public?"*

Of course not. That would be very unhelpful. The ALLOWANCE needs to be applied to what's going on within your own skin. The crazy thoughts and awful body symptoms....

*"But I want rid of the madness and the pain. How would you feel if..."*

I know, I know. But read the paragraph written in bold on the previous page a couple more times. Those things that you are wanting can only be achieved by RE-LAXING - going 'into looseness again' - the pressure has to be vented to bring things back to simplicity, and all of the symptoms that you are experiencing are attempting to create that venting. ALLOW your symptoms.

*"Oh you've got to be having a laugh you crazy therapist. I WANT RID!!"*

Listen to me. There's only one way back to organisation - allow the force of *Unravelling* to do its work. It's producing symptoms that are causing YOU some trouble, but which are attempting to do your system a big favour - the energy that's stuck in your system is attempting to find its way out. Give up the resistance and let *Unravelling* do its work!

*"OK. OK. So how can I give good old 'Unravelling' a little assistance?"*

Would you like to buy a book? Only fifteen quid? Bargain if you ask me....

*************

When we begin to ALLOW symptoms, firstly on the conceptual and then on the actual level - without trying to necessarily 'fix' things - we take our first steps in the direction of a return to an accurate, natural and much more simple response to life's events. When we let ourselves YIELD in the face of painful and disturbing body symptoms, and when we choose to SOFTEN to the deep and disturbing currents of emotional energy that threaten to tear us to pieces from time to time, we start to allow the backlog of energies that have become stuck within our bodies to be let loose back into the deep river of emotional energy.

Although we may instinctually feel, somewhere deep within our system that we're doing the right thing as we hear the faint whispers of the voice of *Unravelling* urging us to 'let go' somewhere just beyond the edges of our perceptions - even with this glimmering of hope and a nugget of faith to support us, the next bit can be a temporary living nightmare. As we remove the pressure brought to bear by our habitual suppression of the emotional energy contained in our system, for a while at least, all hell may break loose.**

I don't know if you've ever dismantled a golf ball. I have. We used to do it when I was a kid. Great fun. Underneath the hard shiny shell there is a tightly wrapped mass of incredibly fine elastic threads - it may even be one continuous thread, I'm not sure. It's this compact mass of coiled elasticity that gives the golf ball its remarkable ability

---

**interesting that the word "hell" comes from proto-Germanic word halja -
"one that covers up, or hides something."

to project itself away from the face of the club when the golfer whacks it. What we used to do was to remove the outer shell, get a sharp knife and lightly slice through the very outer layer of elastic band. The lump would then start to unwind at a rapid rate of knots (haha), spitting out bits of elastic and propelling itself all over the place like a jumping jack firework. It could easily nick your hand if you got too close. As it became smaller, purging toward its empty centre, it would slow, and slow, and then come to rest.

I think that human beings are a bit like golf balls. Our historical disallowing of the four strategies will have produced within us much by way of *compensation*. Every time that we block a natural response to our environment, and operate though a conditioned and unhelpful alternative, we pack a bit more tension into our core. To hold the energy of that tension in place we have to apply a little bit more tension in a slightly different location. We then have to repeat the process again to create a compensation for the last compensation... and so on. In the end we, like the golf ball, will need a very compact shell to keep it all in. And like the golf ball we may look very clean and shiny on the outside, all bouncy and full of energy. But if we were to peel back that shell and make the slightest enquiry into the inner layers....

# BANG!

It is precisely for this reason that many people are scared to death of entering into any therapeutic encounter which would demand looking inward. This is because they can sense the extraordinary amount of energy that is stuck in their system and fear the effects of its movement or release. Unfortunately (and ironically) an unwillingness to make the 'inner' journey may well turn out to be the cause of an untimely and premature demise. The energy will always find a discharge through the manifestation of symptoms on many levels, as we have mentioned above, but there comes a point where the system can take no more - the shell has reached the limit of its operational tolerances and there will be a fracture in the container. This may take the form of a breakdown of internal processes, where the interior of the body suddenly flips into a deeper level of disease process, or may manifest in the form of an 'accident' intruding from the outside, which serves to take the person out of their normal run of things in a sudden and unexpected way.

## Emotional conditioning

When we came into this world, in whatever form we arrived, we were pretty much of a blank sheet. As we got bigger we started being influenced by messages and instructions from those around us, which may have imprinted upon us a bunch of inhibiting 'don'ts', such as:

- Don't be frightened
- Don't get angry
- Don't cry
- Don't get excited
- Don't want too much
- Don't bother

One of these messages probably went in deeper than the rest and became our primary inhibitor, leading to compensatory changes in the other strategies.

For example, if we were told not to be scared, and thereby conditioned to under-react in the face of fear, we may develop an angry temperament designed to keep EVERYTHING away, just in case something was dangerous. In this manner we attempt to avoid anything that may be a threat, ensuring that we don't ever need to call upon the strategy that we've lost the ability to use. So, on being conditioned not to *Move Away* in the face of perceived danger, we have automatically developed an overactive and compensatory tendency to *Push Away*.

The four strategies are exquisitely designed and subtle tools to allow us to orient ourselves skilfully toward the ever-changing environment in which we attempt to survive. If applied successfully, we stay safe, prevent irritants from entering within our circle, and fulfil our needs with regard to nutrition and continuation of the species. In the example above, we unfortunately have lost one tool, and are now using another tool to do a job for which it is definitely not suited. Unfortunately, as they say, when all you have is a hammer, everything begins to look like a nail.

Another example. If our guardians gave us negative feedback toward our natural tendency to *Pull Towards* us our objects of desire, (and subsequently eat or mate with everything in sight) we may learn and come to believe that desire is a dangerous thing. As a result we may again develop a habit of *Pushing Away* quite strongly all interactions, ensuring that we don't ever come up against our 'dangerous' desirous instinct. Problem here is that our urge to *Follow* (which precedes the enveloping process of *Pulling Towards*) will still be operating. Because there is no opportunity for the completion associated with *Pulling Towards*, we may remain stuck in a lifetime of angst-filled longing and emptiness, obsessed with that which we cannot allow ourselves, and inexplicably angry at everything around us.

So when we choose to give up the fight and start to re-cognise and ALLOW the fact that we are in a bit of a pickle, we will then begin to re-lax. We will start to return to looseness *again*. It's not a complex task, but we do need to trust that our system has the innate ability to <u>intelligently reorder itself</u> in the absence of any obstacles that we may have inadvertently, over the course of our lifetime, placed in its way. It is helpful to trust (even if we sometimes doubt) that *Unravelling* is always on our side.

When we give up the fight, and begin to make like an unravelling golf ball, the experience of having to sit in the presence of all the locked-up energy that has been stuck within us as it unwinds can be uncomfortable and frightening. This is the classic 'healing crisis' that is recognised and ultimately welcomed within the world of complementary medicine. When the latest symptoms start to go and old ones reappear for a short while - when the skin, respiratory, digestive and urinary systems begin to show clear signs of detoxification by way of short-term and often highly acute episodes - when previously disallowed emotional responses start to show themselves often in intense and dramatic outbursts for a short time after treatment - when the person begins to show a 'change of heart' toward situations in their lives that seemed to have become intractable - when all that was hidden seems to have broken loose and the person's life seems to have gone completely inverted and they are starting to bear no resemblance to the person that used to look out at them from from the mirror every morning - when all this happens, I have one bit of advice to them. I say...

"Just go with it. It's absolutely safe."

They do. And it is.

They're on the road of wellness now, travelling with a constant and reliable companion who goes by the name of *Unravelling*, padding along faithfully by their side.

# Embracing

So how do we reconcile ourselves with an old adversary? How can we possibly kiss and make up with an aspect of ourselves that we have only known as THE ENEMY for as long as we can remember? Well, hopefully, we now have a little faith that this wayward and unpredictable force which has unleashed so much turbulence in our lives is actually a friend in disguise, and that if restored to its simplest form will steer us gently and surely through our world, keeping us safe and nourished. I reckon a little sympathy wouldn't go amiss. It only shouted because we weren't listening. It had a tiny and wise voice which we chose to disregard, hence its need to develop a vocal style that was a little more, shall we say, demanding of our attention. In seeing its kind, vulnerable and gentle nature, we can maybe begin to offer to it the attention and respect that it deserves.

In 'just going with it' and allowing the maelstrom of inhibited energy to play itself out, as uncomfortable as it has been, we now reach a quieter place. A place where the still, small voice of our emotional intelligence can be heard. It now has only simple instructions to convey and, with our new found listening skills to receive its direction, it will probably have to utter those instructions only once. Eat now. Don't eat that, eat this. Water please. Time to rest. Say no. Nod yes. Don't engage with that person. Turn left. Duck.

If we should ever require the presence of the amplified version of any of the strategies; if for example a charging rhino does actually present itself at the end of the road, then this ramped-up energy will be easily available to us without any fuss or a moment's indecision. And when the emergency is over... then we return once again to centre - to a peaceful and alert state.

# MIND

What's on your mind right now? What images are you seeing with your 'inner eye'? Do you hear voices? (don't be alarmed - it's not that unusual). Your own voice maybe, giving a running commentary on the state of play.

This mental activity of the 'thinking mind' is an interesting thing. Very interesting. In fact it's so interesting that it gets a little bit over-interested in itself at times, and may seem to demand practically *all* of our attention. Attention is also an interesting thing. Attention is the thing that allows us to develop a meaningful relationship with the things that interest us.

We are continually receiving information via sensory experience. This information may arrive via the channel of sight, hearing, smell, or taste, by our sense of touch, or from 'seeing' or 'hearing' the activity of our 'thinking mind'. For us to *fully* register an experience we have to offer our attention to it. More exactly, we have to *mix our attention with it*. The incoming sensory experience, mixed with the focus of attention, allows AWARENESS of an event, making it MEANINGFUL to us.

As you are reading this page, your attention is on the reading. You see the words, and if you're like me, you may hear your own internal voice speaking the words as you read them. Your attention needs to be *highly concentrated* into that process for the reading of the words to become meaningful to you. Through this process you can register how you *feel* about what you have just read. Maybe then you will decide whether you *agree* with the author's viewpoint or not. This process offers the possibility of *learning*.

I remember as a teenager, revising for my history exams and (having little passion for the subject matter) finding it almost impossible to absorb the words that I was seeing on the page of the text book. I would read the same sentence over and over again, attempting desperately to direct my attention and somehow glue it to the task at hand. I might have helped myself by NOT listening to *'The Magician's Birthday'* by heavy rock band *Uriah Heep* at the same time as I was trying to revise. Even turning the music off didn't help much as my attention was much more drawn by the dreamy images of me, lying in a sunny cornfield with Susan Davies, which seemed to run like an unstoppable torrent through my head. Sigh...

Another illustration of the necessity of mixing attention with sensory input to give a meaningful experience, goes as follows. You are talking to your friend. They are looking you in the eye, and are obviously *hearing* the words, but you can tell that they are not *listening*. They are getting the vibrations of the words into their ears but not *paying attention*.

Are you listening to me...?
*"Oh sorry. It's just that I can't get this image of a hayfield out of my mind."*
Did you know Susan Davies as well then?

As you read the words on this page, there are many sensory inputs entering your personal domain. Although your eyes are focussed on the page, your peripheral vision is still receiving signals from events around you in the room, or outside of the window next to where you sit. At some point, something may 'catch you out of the corner of your eye', and cause you to glance in that direction. Your *attention* will go along with that glance.

*"What's that?"*

There are also many sounds finding their way into your ears as you sit reading. Because your attention is heavily concentrated into your visual channel as you read, the sounds entering your ears become just 'background stuff" and don't succeed in drawing your attention away from your engagement with vision. If someone were to suddenly call your name, however, your attention would immediately be drawn to the auditory experience, and away from the visual mechanism.

*"Oy! Baldy!"*

A sudden and unexpected smell of burning would certainly remove your attention from your visual channel. Ever tried to read when you've got an itch between the shoulder blades that just won't go away? Ever tried to settle back and watch a film with a niggling worry running through your mind that won't seem to settle? It's just impossible to concentrate! We can then, usefully define concentration as a wilful focussing (concentration) of our attention toward an incoming sensory experience, with an underlying desire to absorb the information that the experience contains, to create for us a meaningful, memorable or educational experience.

Our attention may get hijacked in many many ways, disallowing us a gentle and easy focus on to the things that we would really like to attend to 'out there' in our world. One of the primary distractions for many people is body pain. Others may be much more distracted by the constant activity of their own inner mental processes. Mental activity can be of a visual nature, taking the form of pictures, or scenarios like little movie vignettes that play over and over again. The inner workings of the 'thinking mind' may also present in an auditory way - monologues, arguments, and scenarios that roll out like scenes from a radio soap opera. For many people, these experiences can be absolutely relentless, and in some cases terrorising and torturing. The constant jabber and argument allows them little rest for their mind, and denies them any sort of easy and pleasurable engagement with others in their world. This can often result in a tragic withdrawal from everyday social engagement.

I have met many people who have been medically diagnosed as 'depressed', and upon enquiry I have discovered that without exception, they have all been stuck in a powerful and all-consuming repeating loop of mental activity. Something has happened, either in recent times or many years ago - commonly a loss, or injustice - and their attention is still heavily glued to that memory. A tendency has subsequently developed within that person to examine the issue over and over in their mind's eye, or to play out alternative, or 'virtual' outcomes to the difficult event. This tendency sucks in most of their attention and a *huge* proportion of their energy, creating a listlessness which eventually discourages them from any attempt toward change.

I remember the words of a teacher for whom I have the utmost respect. He said...

*"The most therapeutic thing that a person suffering from depression can do, is to take up a hobby that involves using their hands"*

I was a bit gobsmacked by this at the time, but now I get it. He was saying that to wilfully place one's attention somewhere (on the manual activity) other than where it is habitually stuck (on the *mental* activity), is remarkably empowering. It allows something to get moving where previously it wasn't. It gives an alternative where there was previously only one option. This change from one to two can sometimes be a kick-start to the person's recovery process, as a third and then further options appear.

An obsessive focus toward the contents of the 'thinking mind' can sometimes be the only refuge for someone who has difficult situations in their 'outer world' that they are either unwilling or unable to face head on. I remember well a couple of long-term diagnosed depressives that I met along the way, one of whom recovered within weeks after (eventually) leaving an unsuitable relationship, and the other after (eventually) walking out of an unsuitable work situation.

I printed out my favourite ditty, which I mentioned earlier, and posted it just inside the doorway of my practice room, so that I can see it when I go in, and my clients can see it on the way out.

> If you always do what you always did,
> You'll always get what you always got.

Nice.

There are many sensory experiences that are deeply magnetizing to our attention. Intense tastes, kaleidoscopic visual feasts, the wonders of music and the sensations of adrenaline flowing through our veins as we launch ourselves from a bungee jump crane. There is nothing, however, that is quite so attractive to our attention as the sea of clutter that goes on between our ears - most of which (if truth were to be told) is utter bilge. The thinking mind, which makes its abode in the cranial vault, is similar to the emotions, in as much as it is a very useful tool. It's not that useful as a survival mechanism for the organism - our emotional strategies deal with that issue just fine. The logical powers of the human neocortex bit of the brain are more suited to the kind of strategy-forming and information-sorting that is necessary for the pursuit of creative acts peculiar to humans - art, technology, philosophy and the like - as well as mundane things like adding up the shopping. If only we could get through all of the clutter piled up in our skulls in order to get some creative work done!

On the most part, our mental space is so taken up by random nonsense - like having a radio tuned in to every single station on the waveband all of the time - that we find ourselves being unable to formulate a creative plan even if we try! It would be nice if we could pick up and engage the thinking mind in the same way that we would pick up a pen, or any other tool. Use it, and then put it down again. It seems instead that our thinking minds are running the show - connected to the mains and switched on twenty four seven, running riot like something possessed!

Maybe we could do with finding a way to pacify our mental world a little. Create some space up there, so we can actually begin to use our minds as a tool for facilitating the amazing feats of creativity that humans are so clearly capable of. If our only experience of our thinking mind is as some sort of crazy garrulous nutcase poking us with a stick every time we try to get to sleep at night, we're hardly likely to want to go into business with it!

The ability to *place our attention*, gently, consistently and wilfully toward a sensory channel - sight, hearing, taste, smell, bodily sensation or mental activity - this ability is at the very foundation of our bodily health, emotional stability, and mental calm. This much maligned and misunderstood skill has been around for thousands of years, and needs for its practice no technology, fancy expensive equipment or special clothes. Just you, and a place to be. It's called meditation.

# AIDS FOR MIND

## Bringing Attention to Mental Processes

For many, an introduction to the notion and practice of 'taking a step back', and non-judgementally 'noticing' the ongoing activities of their mind in 'real time' so to speak, can be a marvellous breakthrough moment.

They may no longer feel stuck *within* the images, stories and dialogues that take up so much of their mind-space. There is a refuge. This process of taking a step back, is in no way a form of dissociating, or an abdication of responsibility for ourselves. It's simply a chance to get an overview, and to give our awareness - the "I" of the Impartial Observer - a chance to operate in healthy concert with the other aspects of our being - body, emotions, and mind.

# Acceptance

Most people are aware to some degree or other of the activity of their internal mental processes - images and running commentaries - but the *content* of that which they witness is often disconcerting to them. The practice of shining the light of full awareness on to this content can often be a tough call.

A person's thoughts may at times be unacceptable, either to their own internal moral code, or the standards that they have inherited from their guardians, family, or culture. The pictures associated with these thoughts may also be disturbing. To stay present to these images may be difficult. Added to this, the voice of internal mental monologue that accompanies many people throughout their lives may have a critical, damning or coercive tone, and is highly unlikely to be welcomed as a friend.

The *acceptance* of all that the mind presents to our observing awareness, represents our *only* hope of quieting our mental world, and bringing a little peace to the craziness that runs riot within the vault of our cranium. Where there is no acceptance, there will be no peace. When we run from anything it *will* chase us. When our attention is actively diverted *away* from the scenarios that our mind presents, we will always be drawn *toward* them. The more we try to distract from this mental content (often by way of addictive activities such as exercise, shopping, sex, drugs, rock 'n' roll etc), the greater the tension that will ensue. We are then actively encouraging a major separation between our mind and our body - between ourselves and our lives - between ourselves and ourselves! This is one of the quickest routes toward illness and breakdown. The mental activity that we are so keen to escape, and to disown is ours. It's 'us'. If we put it away from us, it simply lets us know that we can't ignore it. The harder we try, the louder it will shout.

Acceptance of the content of our minds, as unpalatable as it may sometimes appear, develops the potential for a profound relaxation within our system, encouraging space, ease and response-ability on the level of mind <u>and</u> body - which is the signature of 'good health'.

There is no other sphere of existence in which my favourite maxim

*"just go with it...."*

becomes more apt. Whatever your mind presents to you - glorious, horrific, intimidating, angelic or demonic, recognise it for what it is.

IT'S JUST (YOUR) MIND DOING ITS THING.

You don't need to engage with it, pick it up, play with it, act on it or twizzle it round your finger. It's just STUFF and need not overly concern you.

Disowned mind-stuff can become quite distorted in its attempts to gain our attention. Reminds me of one of those old *Hammer* horror movies where the heroine is being chased through the woods by some beastie or other. She's running like the clappers, and IT is following her with a slow-motion stride. Boomph! Boomph! She's going hell for leather at about twenty miles an hour. Boomph! Boomph! She finally falls exhausted at the base of a tree and the bloody thing's right behind her! How the hell does that work then? Good metaphor though. Just like our heroine, there's no escape from the monsters that we have created in our own mind by our attempts to divert our attention from our unpalatable mind-stuff. Just as the monsters in the films were once just ordinary people who were made monstrous by the mad professor, so our internal demons started out as innocent thoughts and images that were somehow made unpalatable by the mad conditioning of culture and family. In the films, I always wanted the heroine to stop running, do an about turn and say to the beast....

*"What the bloody hell do you want? Don't you know what time it is?"*

and for the beast to say...

*"Well... I dunno really. Hadn't thought it through that far. Just wanted you to know that I was here. Fancy a beer?"*

They go off for a few cocktails, she kisses him, he turns back into the wonderful and simple being that he started off as and they live happily ever after. Hurrah!

My own experience over the years tells me that the greater the level of acceptance that you can muster toward the scenarios, monologues, arguments and images that are presented to you by your own mind, the more spacious and peaceful your mind will become. Over time the nature of your mental activity and the content of sleeping dreams will become more palatable. As the clutter clears, it becomes more easy to use the mind as a tool - to engage it wilfully in constructive and creative trains of thought, instead of continually getting sidelined and distracted by the nonsense.

Reading the above, it all sounds very simple doesn't it? - just notice with full attention the stuff that your mind does, and just let it pass you by like clouds in the sky - easy peasy! However, if you do have a terrorist living in your head, and you haven't been in touch recently, the practice may be a little less straightforward. There are some tricky-to-negotiate responses to an encounter with long-ignored and actively sidelined mental content that are worthy of discussion here.

Scary mind-stuff creates a reciprocal level of scary adrenaline-fuelled feelings in the body. Long term experience of these feelings may result in a huge level of tension and a tendency to *over-control* the muscular system from *bracing* against the feelings. This may result eventually in a *numbing* of deep internal body sensation. When we start to approach and develop acceptance of the content presented to us by our mind, a relaxation deep within the muscular system will start to occur. There will be a profound 'waking up' within a body that has been deprived of normal sensory feedback. The feelings of 'terror' within the body may subside, only to be replaced for a while by painful sensations as the body reorganises its structure and detoxifies in response to the changes. At this stage, many people will convince themselves that *"just going with it"* is a very poor idea indeed!

There may also be a deeper level of disturbance. The response to fearful feelings in the body will *always* result in a tendency to run, fight, or freeze into submission - the classic responses to threat. If we have been sidelining scary mind-stuff for many years, then we may have been 'on the run' or fighting with our world for a good proportion of our lives, exhausting our energy and damaging our health. The body of the chronically fearful person may therefore become progressively dysfunctional, and riddled with pain as time goes by. Addictive activity may then become less and less available as a distractive outlet. The painful and ill body *also* may now have become an undesirable alighting point for our attention, having become an unreliable companion - the 'enemy down there somewhere'. So where can we go for refuge? Often back into the 'thinking mind', but into a mind that is now constantly at war with itself, our attention desperately attempting to keep away from the thoughts that clamour for its gaze. We can then only retreat deeper and deeper into a fortified citadel of mental protection. The person eventually feels imprisoned within a single attic room in a house full of crazies who are intent on partying all night and smashing the place up - threatening at any moment to make their way up the loft ladder. For that person, and tragically, the only way out may be via the skylight...

So when there is no refuge, where to start? This is where bodywork may hold the key. The body of the person described above may have little in the way of pleasurable, or even neutral sensory experience to offer to the person's attention. Everything may have hurt for a very long time, and will probably 'hurt bad'. The experience of receiving skilled touch, whereby a 'good' (or initially 'hurts good') experience can be invoked, is a possible starting point for the reclaiming, and re-inhabitation of this body - a body that has become so uninhabited and discarded due to a long history of pain and unwellness.

This reclaimation process is likely to take some time - maybe years. There will be pitfalls and breakthroughs aplenty along the way. But as the person's attention becomes ever more deeply rooted within the sensory avenues of their body, there is every possibility of an armistice for the beleaguered mind. As the attention becomes more motile, it will develop a freedom and will allow the choice to apply its 'noticing' abilities to more, and different objects - the pleasant feeling of a good dinner in our belly - a lover's touch - the awesome colours of a sunset. When we have a nicer place for our attention to reside, our crazy autopilot mind, with all of its dualities, conflicts and unappealing content will be revealed for what it is - just stuff. The less unnecessary time that we spend in there stirring the muddy water, the more it will settle down. Eventually, its true nature - fundamentally empty of content, like a clear blue sky - will be revealed.

# Silence

The following poem by Wendell Berry, for me, summons up the essence of the processes so far discussed. Brings a a tear to my eye every time I read it.

> *I go among the trees and sit still.
> All my stirring becomes quiet
> around me like circles on water.
> My tasks lie in their places
> where I left them, asleep like cattle....
>
> Then what I am afraid of comes.
> And I live for a while in its sight.
> What I fear in it leaves it,
> And the fear of it leaves me.
> It sings and I hear its song.

Silence reveals to our awareness much that goes unnoticed in the general hubbub of our day to day existence. In silence we can hear the monologue of the thinking mind - its volume, content and insistence quickly becomes apparent. A great deal of this book is about learning to notice more deeply. I have encouraged you to notice the body's language of sensation, and to notice the way that you move your body and

---

---

orient your posture. To notice your emotional responses and the strategies that you operate toward those situations and people that come to meet you in your life, and to notice the content of the inner landscape of your thinking mind - the pictures, words and constructs.

Your endeavours will, I assure you, be greatly enhanced by taking up a formal silent practice.

## Meditation

'Meditation' is one of those words, a bit like 'relaxation' that gets used in a very broad way, even though it has a very specific meaning. If we scan along the bookshelves and CD racks of our local New Age emporium, we will be tempted with a multitude of 'meditations' to calm our fevered soul. All of these offerings, whether they be guides to visualisation, musical, or spoken, are designed to focus our attention - to *bring our attention to something*. This process of *gathering* and *focussing* our attention on to an object is at the heart of meditation practice. That object could be a visual one, such as a candle flame. We may choose a pleasant sound as our object of meditation, or maybe a sensation within our own body, such as the sensation of our own breathing. We could walk slowly in a peaceful area, using the experience of the sensation of our footfalls as our object.

Whatever the object of meditation, our aim is to allow our attention to come to rest on that object - very lightly - just as a butterfly might land on a flower. What we will discover is that this endeavour, although simple, is not quite as easy as we may expect. This is due to the power of *distraction*. Try as we will to gently place our noticing on to the sensation of our breathing, we suddenly find that our attention has been hijacked and that we are in the thinking mind, wondering what to have for supper. On becoming aware of this distraction, we once again return our focus to the sensation of the breath. Thirty seconds later, and we're mentally examining the menu of the local Cantonese takeaway. Oh come on now, let's apply a little discipline here - back to the breath. Ten seconds and that itch under my shoulder blade is driving me mad, and what about that awful conversation I had with Fred today and what's that noise? Oh bollocks the gate's blown open again did I lock the door chicken chow mein.... Aaaaaaarrrghh! (I knew that meditation wasn't for me...)

This is the point at which most people give up their five minute meditation career. They were convinced that meditation was about 'emptying the mind of thoughts' and they have just realized that the chances of emptying their mind are obviously pretty close to zero. So, let us break Meditation Myth Number One. Nobody said that meditation was about 'emptying your mind of thoughts' (and if they did then I'm sorry but they were barking up the wrong tree). The idea is that if we can draw our attention *away* from the thinking mind and *toward* a different area of input (for example the sensation of the breath) then the activity of thinking mind will naturally diminish and become more peaceful. The more attention that is placed on the thinking process, the more it will whip itself up into a frenzy. If you want to see the clarity of the (muddy) water in a bucket, then stop stirring it!

OK so back to the meditation.... breath......bank manager..... oops breath..... mother in law (cold sweat....) come on now focus.. breath...... king prawn chop suey.. mmm.... back to the breath.......................... breath............. breath..........breath...... HEY I'M GETTING THE HANG OF THIS!! WOW! HEY THIS IS JUST WICKED!!!.... O BUGGER!! ......... breath...............breath...........backache........breath.....backache.....    breath......    numb feet.....breath....ouch.....breath.. No I'm sorry that I just can't sit in the lotus position on a rock under this waterfall so I'm obviously not cut out for meditation.

Time to let go of Meditation Myth Numero Deux. Sit comfortably! Very few people are really comfortable sitting on a floor cushion to meditate unless they've done years of Yoga practice. There are some technical advantages to lotus sitting but those are so far beyond the scope of the average urban meditator that it's best to use an ordinary chair to do your practice. It's quite common for body pains and sensations to emerge during sitting practice as the body structures begin to relax a little, and these sensations are amongst the host of distractions that will creep up and vie for your attention during your attempts at meditation. Sitting on the floor just sets you up for more distraction than is practically useful in the beginning. So a nice simple chair - not too hard and not too soft.

If the chair is too comfy, falling asleep is a real possibility. Not that this is a bad thing, but a good proportion of people who set out to practice meditation spend the vast majority of their practice time over the first few months asleep anyway, so we need to discourage that one by not using a gloopy marshmallow recliner for our sessions. Most people's bodies associate the act of closing the eyes with the process of going to sleep, and the majority of the modern population are rather overtired as a generality, so dropping off during the early days of your meditation career is a very common experience. Just go with it. It changes after a while.

So we've learned to bring our attention to the breath. We've noticed that there are many thoughts, concerns and body sensations that marshall themselves to spite our endeavour. Distractions that seem to thwart our every attempt to meditate. And as we all know meditation is about bringing our attention to the breath and keeping it there with unshakeableconcentration..... until.....we.........explode....... AAAARGGGHHH! (again)

Well. Actually, it's not about that at all. So let's lower our expectations a little and explode Meditation Myth Number Three. For all intents and purposes (as an urban meditator) we would do well to assume that there is NO-ONE that we know (unless of course we hang out with someone who has spent thirty years sitting on a rock inside a cave on the side of some mountain in the Himalayas) or are ever likely to know, who is capable of consistently and constantly placing their attention unshakeably on to the sensation of their own breathing without distraction for more than about thirty seconds at a time. So the likelihood of us achieving anything more is fairly remote.

So if we're not going to 'empty our mind of thoughts', free ourselves from the irritating intrusion of distractions into our practice, or create eternal peace within body and mind, then what's the point of doing any practice? The point is this. We are developing our ability to *return to our centre,* by continually exposing ourselves to the CYCLE OF MEDITATION which goes something like this.

- I BRING my attention to the object (say, the sensation of my breathing)

- I BECOME distracted (by thoughts, sounds or body sensations)

- I NOTICE that I have become distracted (my attention no longer on the breath)

- I RETURN my attention to the breath.

The experience of this cycle is the primary reason for the practice of meditation, and the most important bit of all is that MOMENT!! - that flash of awareness as we NOTICE that we have lost our awareness of where we are - the moment that we wake up! Meditation is a practice for the cultivation of greater NOTICING, which is why I believe that next to abdominal breathing practice, it is the most important thing that we can engage in to improve our health.

I favour a practice of simple breathing meditation (employing the sensation of my own breathing as my object) because it kills four birds with one stone - I can get my attention away from the exciting stimulus of my brain, cultivate my noticing ability, improve my awareness of my body, and the mechanism of my breathing in the same session. Win win win win! I like to meditate eyes closed (to reduce distraction) and I find an auditory object (such as music or whale sounds) much less attractive to my attention. The nice thing about the breath is that it is rhythmic, but in a predictable sort of way. It is something that we can 'follow', rather than being a 'point' on which we are attempting to focus. I can register the sensation of my breathing in one of three places. Either via the passage of air through my nostrils, by way of the sensation as the air passes up and down my throat, or (and preferably) the effects of the rhythmic movement of the diaphragm muscle down toward my belly.

Right! So let's get to it! I'm sure that three two hour sessions a day should get me to Nirvana in no time flat! Uh-oh. Time to blow up the final Meditation Myth. Number Four says that more is not better. To be honest, meditation practice, although simple, is not easy. As a martial artist I would consider meditation to be a martial practice. It takes intent, organisation, discipline and persistence. There are times when it feels like the very last thing you want to be doing, and there are times when it drives you nuts. When you start to go into stillness on a regular basis, you really start to notice how noisy your mind is, and you're quickly brought face to face with all of the crazy stuff that it can throw up. When you become more focussed on your body, it will start to offer up for release tensions that may have been lodged in the deep muscular system for many years. When this release happens, it may be uncomfortable. Finally, as we draw our attention ever more deeply into the tidal swell of our breath, it will begin to shed its aberrant and disordered rhythm, and make a return to a fuller and richer wave. It originally became disordered through stress and emotional trouble. As it releases back into its natural shape we may cry, we may shout, we may quake with fear..... and we may well laugh our socks off.

Meditation practice, for all its simplicity, is POWERFUL STUFF. So if you're going to do it, don't do too much for a start. Thirty minutes three times a week. Five minutes sitting to settle down. twenty minutes practice, and then five minutes sitting with your eyes open to return to the day. Best done early morning or evening. Best not done after eating a meal - under these circumstances dozing off is inevitable!

## EXERCISE SIX - BREATHING MEDITATION PRACTICE

Try this

Find a place where there's not too much distraction to sit in your not-too-comfy chair. Switch off phones and tell the family to mind their business for a half-hour. Set a little 'ting' alarm for twenty five minutes. Crack open a window.

Place yourself toward the back of your chair, back well-supported, feet flat on the floor, hands wherever they are comfortable.

Sit for a minute gazing softly into the middle distance and then close your eyes.

Take a couple of slow breaths.
In through the nose...
Out through the nose...
In through the nose...
Out through the nose...

Then, to gather your attention... LISTEN
Listen to the sounds outside of the window. Just Listen.
Allow the sounds to enter your ears, without judgement or naming.
Just Listen. Birds. Cars. Kids. Planes.
Just listen.

Then bring your attention INSIDE of the room.
Again, just listen.
Tick - tock. Central heating burbles. Settling of joists and bricks.

Then bring your attention closer in - into your own body.
Listen.
Gurgles. Your heartbeat. The sound of your own breathing.

Allow your attention to come to the sensation of your own breathing.
At the nostrils OR in the throat OR down in the chest or belly.
FEEL the sensation of the breath as it moves.
Allow your attention to rest gently on the sensation of your breathing, just as softly as a butterfly would land on a flower.......

As soon as you realise that your attention has been distracted away from the breath (by thoughts, a sound, or a body sensations) simply return your attention to the sensation of your breathing.

Repeat.

'Ting'

Take a minute before you open your eyes.
Open your eyes and take a couple of deep refreshing breaths.
Sit for a couple of minutes.
Gently re-enter your day.


I am an inherently lazy fellow, and this has drawn me toward simple things that really do the job whilst taking up a minimum of daily time that may otherwise be more gainfully employed in the eating of Chinese food, listening to Goth-rock, driving a well-sorted hatchback and the like. I wholeheartedly recommend breathing meditation practice to you as a life-enhancing hobby.

TWO

# Obstacles to Unravelling

"It is wise to disclose what cannot be concealed"

Johann Friedrich Von Schille

I've always thought that it would be a real hoot if everyone on the planet had a TV screen above their head, visible to all, showing in real time exactly what was going on in their minds. Imagine it! - chaos would ensue, for a while... *followed by an enduring peace in the world, the like of which we have never seen.* I recently had all of my secrets witnessed by a dear and trusted other. Not just some of my secrets - <u>all</u> of them. I have had only a few really close relationships in my life. Those people knew me partially, but I had never revealed *everything* to another one human being.

I can only describe this event as the single most liberating act that I have ever undertaken in my entire life, and still I cannot believe the result that this 'confession' has had on me. I feel light. I feel easy. I can look other people comfortably in the eye, and speak my needs in a way which I have been unable to do in my life to date.

So what is it about the voluntary freeing of *withheld information* that has been kept (often for many years) within the confines of one's mind that can have such a positive and dramatic effect on one's well-being? Mainly this. It is quite correct to believe that the telling of lies and the keeping of secrets has a profound effect on a person's *psychological* condition, but it is my belief that the more damaging and insidious effect is *physiological* - primarily acting on the *mechanics of breathing*.

Earlier in the book I have discussed the crucial relationship between 'good' breathing and the subsequent optimising effect on the other systems of the body, so no need to reiterate those ideas here. But consider for a moment if you will, the effects of a single lie on the mechanism of a person's breathing. Imagine yourself in this scenario...

Bob and Ali are partners. They live together. They have a computer each. Bob has recently been examining the e-mails sent by Ali from her laptop, (Bob is having unspoken concerns about a possible infidelity). Ali is not aware of Bob's actions but on opening the 'Recent Items' list on her computer, she has suddenly become suspicious...

> Ali      *"Bob? Have you been reading my e-mails...?"*

> Bob      (like a flash) *"No"*

> Ali      *"Are you sure? Because my Inbox was opened yesterday when I was out shopping"*

Now you might think that this fib was the start of Bob's excursion into the world of disordered breathing (having just lied to Ali). But Bob was already in trouble. Having read Ali's e-mails, and having kept that fact hidden from her, Bob's expectation is that Ali will find him out. So, from the point that Bob reads Ali's e-mails, every time Ali says...

"Bob?"

...Bob arrests his breathing rhythm and his adrenaline skyrockets.
When Ali then says...

"What shall we have for dinner?"

...Bob lets his breath go and starts breathing again - but not in a relaxed way, because he's now continually on tenterhooks, just waiting for the next time Ali says...

"Bob?"

So all the time he's with her, for the next x many years, he's holding his breath - just a bit - fuelling all of the detrimental physiological effects that breath-holding creates, and making him a little bit manic in general.

So, let's continue the conversation.

...previously

Ali         "Are you sure? Because my Inbox was opened yesterday
            when I was out shopping"

Bob         Must be a virus in your computer that opened the Inbox.
            I read the other day about that happening to a man who
            lived in Venezuela.... Oh...err.. is that the time? Put the telly on dear."

Ali         "OK"

Now Ali's in trouble. Ali's radar is on full power as she senses a wobble in Bob's voice that makes her think that Bob may be telling porkies and so now she's watching him like a hawk. She goes into a state of hypervigilance, monitoring the subtle instinctual information that her body is giving her during her interactions with Bob. To create enough stillness to notice this subtle radar she breathes out and holds on the outbreath, starving her system of essential oxygen and depleting her energy, depressing her vitality.

This whole "e-mail thing" will get forgotten over time by Ali and Bob - he'll think that he got away with it and she'll label herself as paranoid - but the subtle habits of the disordered breath remain. And the bigger picture, as we have discussed earlier in this book, is that those breathing habits will eventually shape the person's physiology, physiognomy, and their future interactions with other people. Bob will end up with the shape and habits of a man always on the defensive, and Ali may begin to appear rather crushed and wondering why she feels more than a little suspicious of everyone in her life.

OK. We need a happy ending for A & B, so that you, dear reader can breathe easily once again. Where were we? Ah yes...

| Ali | "Are you sure? Because my Inbox was opened yesterday when I was out shopping" |
|---|---|
| Bob | (after three hours and overcome with remorse) "Oh my God yes I did! I'm so sorry sweetheart, but I've just been experiencing this terrible insecurity lately about you seeing another man, and I just had to know so I looked on your computer when you were out yesterday and I didn't think you'd find out and...." |
| Ali | "You nosey ***wit how dare you look at my things. Is nothing sacred you ****ing ****." |
| Bob | "Oh don't shout at me honey bunny I'm so sorry I promise I'll never do it again!" (blub) |
| Ali | "Oh well.... OK..... at least you admitted it. Come on. Let's go for lunch and I'll tell you all about how good Eric is in bed". |

Hmm. I think that maybe we can do better than that.

Ali     *"Are you sure? Because my Inbox was opened yesterday when I was out shopping"*

Bob     **(having read this book and understanding the health-promoting qualities of instant honesty)**

*"Yes. I did. I'm so sorry. I've been having some real insecurities around our relationship recently."*

Ali     *"Oh Bob - how could you. I thought that we trusted each other more than this? But if you're having some worries... let's go for lunch and I'll tell you all about the dreadful people in my new office. Hopefully you'll have no cause for worry then."*

Hey - hang on though! This one's even better!

Ali returns from shopping...

Ali     *"Hi Bob!"*

Bob     *"Oh my God Ali - I've got a terrible confession to make. I've been really worried about our relationship recently, what with you getting a new job and meeting all these new guys and I've..... just looked at the e-mails on your computer because..."*

Ali     *"Whoa there soldier! - Bob - you are such an amazing guy! I'm so lucky to have a partner who can be so straight with me about his insecurities and so quick to own up when he's made a mistake. I love you so much. Come on - I'm going to buy you lunch and when we get back I'm going to \*\*\*\* your \*\*\*\*\*\*s out ... ††*

(†† that's "**sort** your **worries** out" in case you were wondering - naughty!)

But this has to be the best...

> Bob and Ali are so skilled at being constantly honest with themselves and each other that insecurity between them never shows its worried little face. Ali doesn't go shopping today and they spend the whole afternoon (and every other afternoon) getting happily naked. This results in them both losing their jobs and they decide to buy a caravan on the Isle of Sark and start a hugely profitable and environmentally-friendly business growing organic seaweed which turns out to be the much heralded alternative fuel source that saves the planet from environmental catastrophe. They go on to have two wonderful happy and healthy children who, due to their parents' clean and consciously honest approach to living, go on to become great leaders, shepherding humanity toward a glorious and peaceful future. Amen.

Sorted.

# WITHHOLDING

The common link between **secrets, lies** and **unspoken truths** is the **wilful** act of **withholding information.**

Withholding ordinary information from another person is not a problem. For instance, whether or not I have holes in my socks matters little to you, and I feel no real compulsion to offer that particular piece of information out. This piece of withheld information is **neutral.** It has no real **charge** around it.

However, what if I have murdered my mother-in-law and concealed her body under the patio? In this instance, the withheld information is definitely *highly charged,* and the level of charge is directly related to this highly important question:

> What **(DO I ASSUME)** would happen if this information was released from the confines of the privacy of my own mind and presented to the outside world?

In this particular instance, the consequences are fairly obvious and predictable, and justice would probably be seen to be done (m'lud), but what if the consequences of revealing the withheld information are less clear-cut, and based on my fearful assumptions?

Consider another scenario. I have a sexual fetish (pick anything you like here that is of a fairly innocuous nature). No one but me knows about it. It has tormented me for years, not having had an avenue to explore said fetish in the 'real world'. I fear that revealing this information will have consequences that will result in me being outcast from my family circle. I will end up having no intimate connections any more, and my relationships with friends will collapse, I will become recluse, and unwell. I will lose my confidence and be unable to face the outside world. My ability to work and earn a living will be destroyed and I will be made homeless and eventually die, penniless, anonymous and starving, in a freezing gutter somewhere in a desolate grey city backstreet. My final feeling at the moment of my inevitable demise will be one of deep regret, ruining the day that I revealed my "little secret".

My goodness! That's a bit of a leap to take! But I do believe that these chains of assumptions regarding the consequences of revealing something about ourselves that renders us 'unacceptable' to others, are always stacked up and ready to roll out. They do, however, provide a very compelling argument against exposing our secrets!

If you examine with enough scrutiny, the assumed chain of consequences contained within any worry that you care to name, it ALWAYS comes down to a prediction and fear of one's own annihilation. Of late, when I look at the balance of my account on the little slip that accompanies my cash as it's delivered from the hole-in-the-wall at the bank, and my stomach does its familiar little somersault, I have got into the habit of stopping for a moment. I then run through the imagined chain of dire consequences as outlined in the paragraph above. It only takes a few seconds to realise that I am, in this moment at any rate, rather a long way from the 'freezing to death in the gutter' scenario. By doing this, I very soon feel released from my stomach churning paralysis and am free to once more go about my business with a spring in my step.

So back to my... ahem ONE'S sexual fetish. We could do with a happy ending here as well. Here we go. I meet a partner who shares the same harmless fetish as me and we live happily ever after. There. That wasn't too difficult, now was it?

'Withholding' within an individual's system could be likened to an inflated balloon. The containment of the pressurised air by the skin of the balloon is balanced by the air pushing outward and trying to escape. The inflated balloon is at equilibrium for sure, but definitely 'charged' and unstable, as the balloon's elastic nature attempts to discharge the pressurised situation. The more air that is pushed into the balloon, the more potentially explosive the situation becomes.

Withheld information is like this within the confines of our own body-mind system. It **wants** to push out. It's **uncomfortable** to withhold the energy of charged information. It creates **pressure.** It **hurts** to withhold.

We all know what happens when we put too much air into a balloon and exceed the structural limits of the container. We instinctively know this in relation to our own human container, and so this is why most criminals, wrongdoers and ne'erdowells are **dying** ('scuse the pun) to get themselves caught, and usually end up tripping themselves up. They want to let the internal pressure out of the system. Just to deflate, re-lax and regain some equilibrium within the depths of their being.

Although there's a desperate desire to be found out

> *"OK! You got me officer - I did it!"* (**huge** outbreath)

there's also a constant fear of being found out (due to anticipated dire consequences as outlined on the previous page). This situation results in a system full of adrenaline, a tendency to chest breathing and breath-holding, and from there an insidious development of detrimental effects on the many essential physiological processes within the body.

The damaging consequences of a habit of withholding are by now, I trust, fairly clear.

# Secrets,

# Lies,

# &

# Unspoken Truths

**(Telling) "The Truth Will Set You Free"**

*(PG) JC*

---

# Secrets

There aren't really that many types of secrets. To qualify as a fully paid-up secret, the following has to be true...

> "I have had (or am still having) an experience, and I find myself
> unable to reveal the nature of that experience to another person for
> fear of the consequences."

These 'experiences' fall in two two categories. - experiences in our *Inner World*, and experiences in our *Outer World*. Experiences in our Outer World can be placed into three groups:

*1) Things that have I have done to others....*
So what sort of 'things' that we may have done to others would we be reluctant to reveal? Well, they roughly follow the same shape as the Ten Commandments and other religious moral codes. If we have killed someone, stolen something that belonged to another, had an intimate relationship with someone else's partner, without the other person's knowledge, had an intimate relationship with another person outside of a committed relationship without our partner's knowledge, lied about something that may have serious consequences, or violated another's boundaries without their knowledge (like Bob), the knowledge of these experiences may be wilfully guarded within the fortress of our mental world, destined never to see the light of day.

*2) Things that have been done to me by others...*
So what of other people's actions toward us? Those whose boundaries have been violated, especially in a sexual manner, and especially if these events happened when they were still within their family or guardian unit, may be extremely reluctant to report these events. The revealing of abusive behaviour by a family member when we are still reliant on the family unit for our nutrition goes against our natural survival instinct. If we tell all, we may be removed from the family unit and may lay ourselves open to a *far* more life-threatening influence so 'better the devil you know'. Those who are subject to bullying in formative years may also not be inclined to tell. The possibility of retribution and exclusion from the peer group also stirs primal fears of the danger implicit in being 'expelled from the herd'. These tendencies may initiate a lifetime's habit of withholding. As adults, a reluctance to report abusive behaviour by others may turn us into someone who's seen as 'a bit of a soft touch', unable to readily say 'no' and therefore easily exploited by others in our world.

*3) Activities that I am engaged in that are hidden from others....*
These are the solitary (or sometimes group) pursuits, that if revealed to partners, family members, friends or colleagues would (we fear) produce an unfavourable judgement and possible rejection. These are the classic 'vices', which so often result in the partaker of such activities leading a 'double life'. These kind of activities may involve sexual gratification of one form or another, stimulation of the senses through food, drugs or drink, or an involvement in criminal activity, gambling or violence. Many of these would fit into the category that we would call *addiction*.

The kinds of experiences within our *Inner World* that we may choose to keep to ourselves, generally run along similar lines as those of the Outer World. We may find ourselves on the odd occasion *thinking* about bumping somebody off, *planning* to steal someone else's property or seduce someone's husband, or *scheming* a way of breaching another's privacy without them knowing. These mental musings may be fleeting and unbidden - taking us by surprise - or they may turn into obsessive trains of thought or full-blown plans of action which we actively 'run through' in our minds.

Leading a double life is one of the most stressful forms of existence that there is. The internal pressure this creates, can lead, over a period of time, to a total breakdown of physical and mental health. Often people will relieve that pressure by being completely open about their covert activities to a select community of people who are engaged in similar behaviour, and at the same time keep the content of their 'parallel existence' completely hidden from those closest to them. If our nearest and dearest are *not* privy to our secret, then the more *other* people that know, the easier the truth is to bear. However, this poses some risk, and the person may go to great lengths to keep the supporting casts from their two lives at a considerable distance from each other! There will be an enormous level of strain in the mind and body of this person as they attempt to run two stories in the outer world, and manage the information regarding both within their minds. The situation is generally unsustainable, and they usually end up inadvertently tripping themselves up in some unforeseen way, simply in order to burst the bubble of deceit and regain some sort of equilibrium within themselves. The deceit can often create the backdrop for tormenting dreams, as the defences of waking consciousness are lowered during sleep. Someone once told me that he has always addressed all of his intimate partners (wives <u>and</u> lovers) as 'sweetheart' and trained himself to never use their first names. That way, if he turns over in the night and mutters someone's name other than the person he is sleeping with it'll never cause a problem. Smart cookie. I think he's doing time in jail now so doesn't really need to worry about that particular problem any more (I hope...).

## Compensation and delusion - the 'split' personality

For the solitary keeper of a secret, the outlook can be far darker. They absolutely believe that if they were to disclose the information they are holding, there would be some very bad consequences, and therefore the 'thing' that constitutes their secret must in itself be a 'bad' thing. However, they will also have in some way managed to delude themselves that the activity that they are involved in, and the withholding of that information from others is 'OK' to some extent. To have 'bad' and 'OK' sitting right alongside each other in one's mind is a very hard thing to bear.

The personality and behaviour that we present to the outside world is to a large extent a reflection of our mindset. If we have an *opinion* that all traffic wardens are bad people, it's likely to show to some degree on the outside. We walk back to our car, and he's in the process of writing a ticket. If we don't harbour the opinion stated above we simply walk up to him, and accept our fate gracefully, in the knowledge that we screwed up (again). If however, we have convinced ourselves that these people are the spawn of the devil, then, as we approach we start to respond with the emotional strategy of *Pushing Away* - the fight is on! Adrenaline flows, blood pressure rises, face pinkens and breath becomes short. Our bodies tighten, arms start to wave, and what then issues forth from our mouth toward the poor warden perfectly reflects the internal state of craziness that is beginning to fire up in our system. The outcome to this story could go many ways, but none of them will be very pretty or conducive to relaxation and happiness!

The key issue here is that the whole scenario unfolded as the result of my *conditioned and fixed opinion*. I will posit this opinion as my truth, and may even see it as THE TRUTH, but in essence it's only my opinion, and the traffic warden's black eye is a manifestation of the consequences of that opinion filtered through my skewed emotional responses finding their way into my physiology. If my opinion were THE TRUTH then everyone would behave this way, but they don't do they? No. So it's just an opinion. One of the great benefits of the awareness that arises from acknowledging the presence of the Impartial Observer in our lives, is that we can begin to _notice_ the effect that our mindset and our opinions are having on our behaviour, and accurately evaluate the results that we are consequently reaping from our actions. In noticing, we begin to create some space between our opinions and our behaviours - a chance to rid ourselves of the often damaging 'knee-jerk reactions' toward people and toward the events that come to meet us in our lives. In this way, we may save untold numbers of traffic wardens from a lifetime of unnecessary suffering.

So, for the solitary secret-keeper - that person with the devil on one shoulder and an angel on the other, with 'bad' and 'OK' living in adjacent rooms in their mind - well, the personality of that particular person may display some rather interesting and contradictory aspects. As we have seen from the traffic warden scenario, the views that we hold in our mind <u>drive</u> the responses of our being on the levels of movement, speech, and behaviour. Having very fixed opinions about the world may make us a difficult character to deal with, but having a mindset with two contradictory views that are only showing themselves by way of compensation for each other makes for a very confused and confusing person indeed! We cannot show the 'bad' as that would mean attracting attention to our withheld secret, and the 'OK' only came into existence by way of compensation for our view of the 'bad' so it in itself is not 'OK' at all! Yoiks!

So what do we see on the outside? Probably a person who tries desperately to be 'nice all of the time' and possibly rather accommodating - a little bit sickly sweet maybe, and yet in their presence we have a definite sense of unease. They may be very distractive, using speech, humour and body movement to hypnotise and beguile us, distracting us away from that which we may see if we were to look deep enough into their eyes.

But above all, this person will be exhausted. The energy it takes to keep these plates spinning is just phenomenal. There will be a huge level of underlying depletion and tension in the body arising from their disordered breathing, and simply from the sheer effort of maintaining the facade. The physiological damage from all of this disorder will be insidious. This person will not be getting weller as time goes by, but will be heading for trouble, which in all fairness may not show until they are in their middle years. The amazing ability of the human system to accommodate disorder within its walls may protect them from crisis until one day the operational tolerances are exceeded and...

*"Who'd have thought it would have happened to Maurice - his heart just gave up - two o'clock in the morning while he was sitting in front of his computer. He was so healthy an' all. Ate well, didn't smoke or drink, went to the gym sixteen times a week... and he was such a helpful chap. Did you know he'd been a scoutmaster for thirty years..."*

## To Tell Or Not To Tell?

So then. What would we be wise to reveal? What should we keep to ourselves? The key question is this...

> "Does the withholding of this piece of information diminish
> my ability to relax in this moment?"

If the answer to this question is a resounding YES, it's worth considering getting the information 'out there' in some form so that you may breathe out, and then breathe easily once again!

The answer to the question does, however, probably vary depending on who you are with at the time. If you live completely alone on a desert island that is well-stocked with food, and enough stuff to stop you going out of your mind with boredom, then you could probably be stuffed full with secrets and still find the ability to be very relaxed. However, no man is (on) an island (haha), and most of us have to deal every day with other people ranging from those intimates in our lives, to complete strangers. If we are surrounded by strangers, then secrets become far less charged. This is why some folk have a desire to go off and 'start a whole new life' well away from the area and people that they know, and from those who know them.

There is one slight flaw in that particular plan however. Digressing slightly, my wife and I spent many hours last winter conducting research (ahem) for this book down at the local pub. Our local is a 'proper' pub - no food served, and it's rammed every night with people drinking and actually talking to each other like they used to in the old days before pub menus started to have fish and chips and fajitas on the same page. Consequently there's a general hubbub of noise in the place, and everyone's talking pretty loud. We noticed quite by chance one evening that there are certain words which, when uttered in conversation, obviously show up as a 'ping' on the internal radar of a good proportion of those present, catching hold of their attention, and resulting in a miniscule and momentary hush in the general cacophony. We've tested this out thoroughly and found that the words "sex" (obvious one), "affair" and "cash" are the most potent by far. My reason for mentioning this is that if you do 'start over' in a new town 'where no-one knows your name' and you are the owner of an *enormous* great secret, then you may be forever sitting on eggshells, hanging off tenterhooks (mix them metaphors boy), and spooking every time someone in the bar utters the words "under" and "patio" in close succession. There's no escape for the keeper of a real whopper.

In closer company - family and friends - there may always reside a fear within us that our secrets will be discovered - that we will be 'seen', exposed, and consequently rejected, with all of the potential for inevitable personal annihilation that this exposure has to offer. This will affect our behaviour towards those closer others - particularly toward family members. Rejection by our parents, when seen from the perspective of our 'inner child'*, would result in starvation, so whatever you do don't court rejection from your parents (pretty sound survival strategy I reckon). For this reason, keeping secrets from one's parents comes quite naturally to most people. We usually justify this by saying to ourselves..

*"Well. They're getting on a bit and I wouldn't want to upset them."*

Shame really - and a shame to have kept the secrets from them for so long. It would be nice to have a lifelong association with our parents that is centred around relaxation and ease of breath, and subsequently enjoying as a family unit all of the health benefits and inter-generational happiness that this would bring about.

As we have discussed earlier, if we are harbouring a highly charged secret, there's always a fear of the assumed consequences of that secret being revealed. In the presence of our parents or guardians, it's an obvious and constant worry After all, they've been the ones who've observed our development as we've grown, so they *obviously* know everything about our history and can *surely* see into the deepest recesses of our minds and are *at any moment now* about to reveal to Auntie Flo and Uncle Jim the full extent of the darkness residing within their darling demon prodigy!!

Sorry. Got a bit carried away then. But you can see why many people try too hard to keep their parents sweet and (probably) let them get away with all sorts of unreasonable behaviour in the bargain - and then blame the unreasonable behaviour on their parents. What a cheek!

So what about keeping secrets from our kids? Possible rejection by our children is probably not a survival issue, but who wants to die at ninety years old with no-one except an overworked nurse by our bedside? Do you recognise these familiar justifications for not revealing secrets to your kids?

---

* I always work on the assumption that there is an aspect of my behaviour that is still conditioned by the experiences accumulated during the first few years of my life.

---

or

*"They're too young to understand."*

or

*"They wouldn't understand."*

or

*"They've got busy lives."*

or

*"What they don't know won't hurt them."*

The last one particularly demands a little scrutiny. Heard the one about the man who 'took his secrets to the grave'?

## FACT - SECRETS DO NOT GO TO THE GRAVE

How could they? They are constantly being kept alive and very well thank you in every disordered human breath.

The issue around keeping secrets from our kids is a tricky one. If we are parents in a couple, then to jointly reveal a secret to our kids suggests that we have been holding that secret *as a couple*. The secrets that couples hold jointly within their circle of two are usually not about themselves, but about the couple's parents or other relatives. Revealing these secrets is risky, as the couple may not want the the parents or relatives in question to know that they are aware of a supposedly well-kept 'family secret'.

More often, secrets within couples take the form of one member of the couple keeping a secret from their partner. If one partner was to tell the kids their secret, it makes revelation a much more risky proposition - 'fessing up to the children may risk rejection not only by their kids, but also their partner *and* the parents. Just for good measure, how about the one where one parent in a couple reveals a secret to their children (or to just one of them), and instructs the kids to keep the information to themselves for fear of 'hurting someone's feelings'!

At this point, '...death in in a freezing gutter somewhere in a desolate grey city backstreet' can seem strangely preferable to the hell of confusion and compensation, misinformation and just the whole amount of energy that it takes to keep all of those plates spinning within the lifespan of a family unit. And of course, in truth, we know that a family (notwithstanding certain tragic circumstances) does not have a lifespan. Family goes on, and the cancerous effects of the secrets go on, from generation to generation. Eventually, the actual informational content of the secret's story may be lost, but family members have got used to tiptoeing around each other, with everyone holding their breath and wondering why the hell they all feel so ill.

What a mess.

Some of the most tragic and abhorrent behaviour that we ever become aware of (usually via the media) is where a couple is engaged in abusive behaviour toward their family or other vulnerable beings, and then decide between themselves to keep their secret from the outside world. The damage that one person can inflict upon humanity is quite considerable, but their reign of terror is generally and mercifully short-lived. The abusive activities of a larger group of people (unless the group is secluded) are often brought into the light by a disaffected group member, and therefore becomes visible and remains under the scrutiny of the outside world. Sometimes this puts an end to the abuse, sometimes not. The activities of a secret-holding, collusive and abusive couple within a family unit, however, may go on for years and years, deeply blighting (and too often ending) the lives of those who fall under its malign influence.

Finally, when one section of a whole nation becomes infected by the savage effects of a deceitful opinion held by one influential leader... well, the results of this are well-documented and need no further discussion here. But to entertain the possibility that we can trace the genesis of the extermination of a whole population of living beings to the withholding tendency of a single person who showed up at a particular juncture in history at just the wrong moment...?

To take a further step toward controversy: would we be justified in viewing the dreadful hells of war that have swept through nations from time to time during human history in the same way that we would consider symptoms within our own bodies - as the only possible method by which the hidden can emerge into the light - the only way that the larger collective 'body' of the world can become weller? *Unravelling* drives a hard bargain.

We are all victims of the withholding process. We are wilfully self-traumatised as a result of the internal pressure generated by the withholding of charged information, and damaged by being subjected to the confusion generated as a result of spending time in the presence of those who withhold but would claim otherwise.

So, next time you get an opportunity to withhold - don't... and see what starts to happen in your world.

## Breath Entrainment & Resonance

During the early stages of my bodywork practice, I noticed a curious thing. During sessions with some clients, I started to feel unwell. I would get a bit dizzy, develop a mild headache, and start to feel anxious and a little woolly in my thinking processes. I had heard that it was possible to 'pick up bad energy' from clients who were unwell, but this theory sounded far too fluffy for my scientific brain and I was having none of it. So I started to observe myself a little more closely.

I noticed that when I was with these clients I had unconsciously moved away from utilising my diaphragm to breathe 'into my belly', and had gone into chest breathing. In some cases I was actually holding my breath for short periods of time. I clocked which clients this was happening with, made a conscious effort toward full belly-breathing when I was in their company, and the ill-effects disappeared.

I also noted that this group of clients seemed to experience far less improvement and benefit from the bodywork that I was offering than those with whom I felt more at ease. As I have posited relaxation as a primary factor in the improvement of health, you can see where all this is pointing. For the client to be able to start to relax in the therapist's company is an absolute prerequisite to any successful therapeutic intervention. The therapist should ideally be the more relaxed one of the two people present within the therapy room, otherwise there's not an awful lot that he or she can do for the other person.

I read some years ago about the phenomenon of *breath entrainment*. It has been noted that mothers can use their own slow and relaxed breathing rhythms to soothe their young children. My own feeling is that if you put two people in a room together for any length of time, one person's breath pattern will start to become more like the other person's. They may reach a place where both of their breath patterns are different to the ones that they started out with - a middle ground, so to speak, or one person may end up completely entrained with the other. My own experience with my clients as outlined above has made me very conscious of this phenomenon, and so in my therapy room I'm gently determined to stick with my slow and full diaphragm breath. By secretly offering this to them as a good example, the therapeutic intervention is hopefully off to a good start! But I keep a sharp eye out for the stressed-out chest breather nowadays, and remain vigilant to my tendency to be drawn into other people's patterns of breathing.

## Family Secrets & Conspiracy

I have a strong belief that breathing rhythms and styles are unwittingly copied within family units. It makes sense to me that this is the case. We see recurring patterns of movement, muscular development, physiognomy and speech in families. Much of this happens through copying by the child in the early years of their development. When you're little, you inevitably look up to those nearest to you to see how to be. Underlying the patterns that are easily available to be seen and imitated, is the less obvious and subtle undercurrent of the breath. The breath pattern of each person is as individual as the person around which it is shaped, but the fundamentals of our individual breathing pattern are likely to have been established very early on in our lives, and much of what develops will, in essence, be copied and absorbed from those with whom we spend long periods of time. The primary process that determines the quality of our physiological well-being - our breathing - has become *conditioned* without our even noticing!

So is this why *behaviours* and *traits* are 'inherited'? Via an affected and conditioned physiology? It is natural to emulate patterns of movement, and inevitable that we may imitate language styles and content, and absorb opinions and beliefs. But what if the deeper motivating forces, especially those darker elements involving untruths and 'secret' behaviours were passed along to us by the undercurrent of the breathing patterns of those guardians who surrounded us in early life?

We are all born into the disordered breathing patterns of the guilty. I don't know who said that. It may have been me, but I feel it as a truth. What this implies is that those like myself, who grew into this life with odd behaviours that they found to be addictive and uncontrollable, that they did not understand and could not account for historically, even after submitting to the delvings of the therapeutic process, may be helped enormously by recognising their tendencies as having been 'passed on' possibly from many generations previous. This is of course not aimed at shifting the blame for harmful or hurtful actions. We all did stuff to others and we all got stuff done to us. That's history and the facts are not going to change. The question is, how are we going to go beyond blame or self-recrimination, breathe easy again, and find a way to break the chain of harm and self-harm?

# Lies

Telling lies is based purely on the following thesis.

*"Something bad will happen if I tell the truth."*

The "bad thing" that will happen is either, as we have previously discussed, the inevitable annihilation resulting from complete rejection by our loved ones and the rest of society, or it may be the immediate anticipated reaction of the person standing right in front of us, followed (of course) by the whole "dying in a freezing gutter somewhere in a desolate grey city backstreet" scenario.

Even those not in the habit of lying may drop the occasional whopper after having done something stupid and feel mortified at the anticipation of inevitable embarrassment from exposing their antics to another...

*"I have NO idea what's wrong with that silly car..."*

and then later we find out...

*"Yes I actually did fill the car with diesel......again........sorry."*

(...after the car was booked into the garage due to a mysterious engine failure that cost a grand to put right). But in this instance, the person lied initially because he was justifiably terrified of the stock reaction from his wife, so fair enough!

Habitual and constant telling of lies is remarkably stressful. If we are to remain undiscovered then we will have to remember accurately what we told, as we will probably be called upon to re-create that made-up story to everyone who sits within our web of fabrication. We will have to get into the habit of storing that information for regurgitation. This 'standby' mode in the mind - never allowing ourselves to forget the storyline for fear of getting caught out - puts a huge mental strain on the habitual liar.

If we are *not* in the habit of lying, we can afford to let go of the narrative surrounding whatever experiences we have, as the *real* truth is always easy to recall. This is because the memory of our experience of *actual* events is registered in real time by *all of our senses* - sight, sound, smell, taste, and associated body sensations. In other words, our *whole being* is used to retrieve 'true' memory for recollection and recounting to another person. This means that there is no need for *fabrication* and subsequent storage of information as a memorised mental narrative, which is precisely what occurs in the case of a lie.

The liar is a fabricator of stories. These stories are created on the mental level only, with a narrative and accompanying fantasy images within the mind of the liar - the stories do not relate to 'real' experiences, and so do not have any actual sensory basis, or associations. The story has therefore to be remembered, as a narrative. This is why those who lie are often unconvincing. Someone recollecting a *true* story, and recounting an *actual* experience will be cueing into the sensory associations of that experience, and will appear animated and engaged with their eyes and body language. During the relaying of a fabricated story, the liar may appear a little stilted. Remember, as we said earlier on, there is only one reason for hiding the truth; namely, the fear of the assumed consequences of exposing one's inner reality. With regard to secrets, this withheld inner information could be one of any number of things. In the case of lies, the withheld material is information regarding the *actual* nature of an event or experience.

The deeply habitual liar, *finds it almost impossible to be truthful, as their habit is to be untruthful.* I know that sounds like an obvious statement, but I point again here toward the *habit* of lying. Because being truthful is a near impossibility for the liar, he or she is more and more led toward deceptive behaviour that will inevitably breed even greater levels of deception. If this wasn't the case there would be no fuel for the habit! There is a strong possibility that the tendencies of the habitual liar may become so entrenched that they end up as a complete fantasist, as their personality becomes hijacked, and is transported lock stock and barrel into the virtual world of their mental narrative.

This tendency toward holding narratives in the memory, trying to remember who's been told what, and the creation of alternative realities is a long and slippery slope towards a complete malfunction of the mental processes, and may lead toward a complete breakdown, where interpretation of 'actual' events in real time becomes severely distorted, and the person's reality ceases to be shared by any others in their world. I have a strong sense that a lifetime habit of lying, and the holding of various versions of 'reality' within the mind, may be a strong contributory factor in the kind of breakdown of mental functioning observed in senile dementia. To make an analogy - if one were to use one's hand in a clearly dysfunctional way for many years - I dunno, something like holding it in a fist for twenty four hours a day - it would eventually cease to function as a hand. Using our brains to process untrue narratives to report to others, alongside our real sensory experience of events is not really what the brain was designed for. I can imagine that under these circumstances the brain would eventually become 'worn out' and would begin to lose its ability to accurately process real-time information. Our big outer brain is the most recent aspect of our evolution. Perhaps we can be forgiven for not quite having got the hang of using it it yet.

The detrimental effect upon the physiology within the body of the liar should also not be underestimated. The extreme level of directed attention toward the mental sphere of activity, which is necessary to sustain accurate maintenance of fabricated narratives, will deprive the rest of the body of due awareness. As we have stated earlier, this will diminish circulation of the blood, affect the assimilation of nourishment via the guts, reduce detoxification and lower vitality.

So why the habit? What is the genesis of this most destructive of behaviours? Telling lies creates no *real* advantage for the liar, but there must be a *perceived danger* around being exposed that seems *exceptionally* real. It is highly possible that the consequences of a previous exposure somewhere in their personal history may have left them with an *innate terror of exposing themselves to another.* They may then put in place an internal strategy that says, quite explicitly:

**If I reveal my true self to another, then my life is at risk. Period.**

What could be the origin of such a DEEPLY ingrained belief?

Let's see.


## Withholding Revisited

Big problems don't just appear from nowhere. Big things grow from little things. The shoot that appears from a germinating acorn is pretty simple, and very tiny. All baby oak shoots look pretty much the same. As they grow, they are shaped by influences and events in their immediate environment. This is why all big oak trees look different (although they retain similarities that makes them recognisable as oak as opposed to beech or birch). They end up different shapes, have varying life spans, and accumulate different scars from their life's trials. Much like humans. We begin small and simple. We respond in a simple way to our local environment, initially caring little for anything other than comfort that arises from being warm, and feeling a sense of fullness in our tummy.

As these foundational and fundamental needs are regularly established, we will then have the freedom to develop and explore the sensory channels that our human biology offers. The myriad of visual and auditory experience through eyes and ears. We experience tastes and smells, and our awareness is magnetised toward the sensations within the internal environment of our own bodies. Our natural inclination toward that which is pleasant and pleasurable, and away from that which irritates and grates begins to develop within us, choices - preferences. I like sour, not so keen on sweet. I am drawn by pink, but blue I find less comfortable on this exploring eye. My guardians are heard to say...

> *"He's not a typical boy is he? He doesn't go for blue!"*

and

> *"Oh, don't give him that. He won't eat it. It's too sweet."*

*As I become more and more secure and established in this growing body, my warmth and nutrition assured, my sensory world is my playground and laboratory. Sights, sounds, tastes, smells, sensations and the images from my dreams exploding into my awareness as a fantastic kaleidoscopic panorama of experience.*

*The body channels awaken. I am free... the whole of my existence is seething with sensation and expression of movement and sound. My guardians delight at the innocence of my ecstatic demonstration of the bliss of being alive and aware within a tiny human frame.*

*My mouth awakes. The texture of custard and jelly. The rightness of eating soil and pencils. The "this is different to that but everything just feels so..... GOOD in my mouth!" The worm in my mouth - a step too far. Toward some things, away from others.*

*My skin awakes. The sensation of feather and blanket on lip. The feeling of hot tarmac on my belly and sunshine on my naked back floods me with pleasure. The sand of the beach between my bare toes - just too much!! Away from some things, toward others.*

*My hands wake up. They explore with their dexterity the textures of everything within reach. The softness of the kitten's back. The shudder through my body as my nails encounter chalkboard. Toward some things - away from others.*

*I explore myself. My hand explores my skin. Pleasure in my hand. Pleasure in my skin. This absorbs me - demands my attention. Pleasure magnified and intensified by the hand/skin/hand/skin relationship. My mouth and face so sensitive. My chest. My genitals.*

---

*It absorbs me. Pleasure creates pleasure. It absorbs me. This pleasure creating pleasure. No reason to stop. I have found a resting place. This is my sole direction. Towards pleasure. Away from pain or anything else. It absorbs me. It...*

# "Stop that! It's dirty!"

## (the hand is smacked and yanked away)

*I reel.*

*Time stands still. Pleasure and pain collide like twisted metal and splintered wood. I see the anguished expression on my guardian's face, looming above me.*

*I was sure and now I'm not so sure. I didn't know I was sure until now I feel unsure. Before now sureness wasn't even an issue. Up to now my guardians have provided me with warmth, nourishment and physical protection to ensure my survival. If I ever overstepped the boundaries of safety, as my curiosity launched my hand toward the hotplate, or my wayward foot strayed toward the kerb on a busy road, I soon learned what 'not to do'. I wouldn't thank them until much later, but clearly knew what 'not to do'.*

*This was obviously another one. Hand to skin pleasure. Another 'not to do' instruction. They never reacted this way to my obvious taking of pleasure from the warm sun or sloppy ice cream down my chin - they seemed very happy and relaxed about those things. So they obviously can't be displeased with with me feeling pleasure? Must be about 'touching skin' or 'down there' or maybe both! It's obviously highly dangerous - they've never reacted like this. If they see me 'touching skin down there' they may become so displeased that they will abandon me - even kill me. Maybe I'll die if I 'touch skin down there'.*

*I'll not do that again.*

*But other pleasures pale into insignificance... what to do?*

*Best keep it secret.*

It may be that I'm the only one who identifies with the above. I suspect that I'm not. If I am, then thanks for listening - I feel so much better now! I'll put you a cheque in the post and call you next week for another appointment.

As children we are little buckets of wonderment, and our curiosity knows no bounds. The child in our story had up to that point, an open and positive response from his guardians to his exploration of the world. They delighted in his pleasure. The defining moment came when the guardian reacted to their experience of witnessing his self-exploration, in an unexpected, conditioned and punishing manner. His nicely developing learning circuits registered that the pleasure gained from self-exploration of the genitals was DANGEROUS.

This was, of course not true, but it had now become a truth for the child. Subsequently, the innate biological programming that took his organism toward pleasure and away from discomfort was now somewhat discombobulated. His self-exploration was the most pleasurable experience of his short life - eating jelly and putting pencils up his nose paled into insignificance in the face of this glorious technicolour experience. So he was hardly likely to give it up and settle for less.

And so, the joys of self-exploration became an activity hidden from the eyes of the world. The initial reaction and punishment of the guardian made the boy's self-exploration a deadly and potent mix of pleasure and anxiety. As the boy's mind developed in both its complexity and capability, he learned that the sensual exploration of self was only a starting point for a whole myriad of interactive possibilities involving others. Woohoo! But the secretive nature of his self-exploration, and *fear of his own sexual feelings* tainted the whole of his view toward this burgeoning facet of his life. Even a thought of pleasure from sexual activity (of which at this stage there were many and often), brought with it a deep apprehension, and a developing resentment toward the very mind that generated such thoughts and fantasies, accompanied by an even deeper suspicion of the sensual fleshy body from which these torments had their genesis.

Eventually, any thought from within about sex, any mention of sex by others, any slight visual association with sex that stirred the sensations within the body became THE ENEMY, and was to be avoided at all costs.

We should remember at this point that the subject that has now become the focus of the words on these pages and has acquired the label 'sex' did not start off this way. It began as the expression of a young child's wondrous exploration of the glorious world of sensation within his own body. Originally it was an experience of the flow of pure vitality. Now it has become the Devil incarnate.

*"My body is now my adversary - and yet it remains, like a mistrusted neighbour. My vitality/ sexuality is now a threat - I will have to suppress it to survive. My sensation and pleasure is dangerous - and yet it draws me like a magnet. My mind is full of dangerous poison - I must replace its contents with... well anything with sufficient power to keep my thoughts away from matters of the flesh (either my own, or that of others)."*

The key point that I would like to extract from the above scenario is this:

ANTICIPATION BY THE INDIVIDUAL OF POTENTIAL REJECTION
BY THE GUARDIAN, IS FOR ALL INTENTS AND PURPOSES,
A LIFE-OR-DEATH ISSUE, AND **WILL** ELICIT A SURVIVAL STRATEGY

In other words, if I observe a highly charged and apparently hostile reaction from my guardian to either my behaviour, or my mere presence, and (being little) am therefore unable to run or fight, I am most likely to enter into a submissive state - quietening the breath and diminishing my movement, or even freezing, so as to not be considered a threat to the angered being standing before me. Even after the event I will probably make an 'unconscious choice' to dumb down the free and spontaneous expression of my life's energy. I may also catalogue deep in my memory banks the type of behaviour that elicited this reaction in the guardian and carefully ensure no repetition.

At worst, and later in life, the scars of this type of experience may be clear for all to see. I may be subjected to the terrors of this same heightened and paralysed adrenalin-fuelled state of panic within my body every single time I perceive a negative response toward me by another person. As my internal vitality is stirred, through sexuality or other stimulating activity, it may bring about an immediate shutdown in my systems. Even the fun of a social gathering or the sound of loud music may be a trigger for withdrawal. The 'sensitive' individual with an 'intolerant' physiology may be reliving every day the trauma of an anticipated annihilation which occurred long, long ago.

For the child whose experience was one of violence, sexual abuse or actual abandonment by the guardian, the potential for the outcomes as described above will be significantly increased. However, for those fortunate enough to have not encountered such maltreatment as a child, a *perceived* threat of abandonment, (which may be activated simply by virtue of the guardian's absence due to work, illness or the demands of siblings, or even their indifference or lack of attention to the child due to a preoccupation with their own internal issues) may leave a similar, albeit less deeply entrenched wound.

For a very young child, panic in the face of potential rejection or abandonment is a completely appropriate response. Rejection of a child before the stage at which it can keep itself warm and feed itself represents clear and present danger, and would result in the actual demise of that child. So at what age does this issue become irrelevant? That's a difficult question to answer. Many people retain complete financial (and therefore nutritional) dependency on their guardians for a large proportion of their adult lives - some for the whole of their lives, and therefore some may always show a fear-driven response to a withdrawal of the guardian's attention.

For wild animals, things are much more simple and clear-cut, although much more edgy! The mother initiates an instinctive weaning of the young animal - a 'pushing away' process. If the youngster does not develop the requisite feeding skills in the time span that would be observed as normal for that species, it will not survive - and that, as they say, would be that. This makes perfect sense. If young wild animals were to develop the kind of complex and long term dependencies that we accept as commonplace in the arena of the human family, this would present danger not only to the youngster, but also to the mother and to the rest of the herd.

So for humans, the possibility of rejection by the guardian may be perceived as a very real survival issue for as long as the weaning process has not been completed. Hopefully, as young adults, and with a little consciousness on the part of our guardians, we encounter the opportunities that allow us to 'find our feet', begin the process of creating our own nutritional base, and make an appropriate distance from those who cared for us as youngsters. We are then well on the way to creating our own brand new 'herd'. For some, sadly, this is not the case, and as the years go by, the impending and inevitable death of the elderly guardians may initiate a severe crisis for the 'adult child'.

For some teenagers, depending on their constitution, their reaction to the perceived indifference of, or dangers created by being in the presence of an emotionally unstable guardian will produce an explosive 'self-weaning' - a propulsion *away* from the guardian's world into a new (and often challenging) arena where their attempts to learn about self-support must of necessity be highly accelerated!

Another opportunity to shut down one's own vital energy by neatly side-stepping the developing arena of sexual expression, presents itself with the onset of puberty. At this stage of life (in our half of the hemisphere at least) the emphasis is firmly placed on education of the academic kind. The pressure is high, as are the expectations of teachers, and guardians. To keep the *approval* of the guardian, (and thereby avoiding their anger and potential abandonment followed quickly [according to the insecure child within] by starvation and death) teenagers may make the skewed choice of exclusively pursuing their educational endeavours to the exclusion of all else even in the face of rampaging hormonal activity! This may displace the 'normal' development of sexual exploration with others, and the person's sexual expression may become more fantasy-driven and secretive. Sex may again become something 'bad' and best covered up.

## On Being Lied To...

The detrimental effects on the general well-being of the habitual liar are, I am sure by now, quite clear. Withholding, by way of wilful deception creates negative effects on our physiology, our psychology and on the quality of the life experiences that reflect back to us from our environment. When we hear reports of a spectacular deception either in the news, or more locally from friends of family members, we generally feel sorry for the victim of that deception. For example, when a friend has uncovered infidelity on the part of their spouse or committed partner, we naturally extend sympathies to our friend. Their partner must have been an exceptionally good liar. How is it that our friend could have been with that person for so many years with such a level of deception playing out right under their nose? Actually you know, that's a very good question. I would posit the view that all of us, somewhere deep within, absolutely know when someone is telling us a lie. We are all hardwired with an internal radar which has been purpose built to pick up on the unique frequency of deception.

So if that's the case, why do so many people overlook the dishonesty of intimate others in their lives for such a long period of time? They obviously have good reason for doing so. As we have seen, our actions and decisions are based on emotional survival strategies, and therefore the tendency to live with what, from an outsider's point of view, looks like an intolerable level of deceptive activity by those close to them, must be underpinned by a thesis that goes something like this:

> "If I expose the dishonesty that I know is being perpetrated
> by Person X, then something very bad will happen to me"

So what may this 'bad' thing be? Surprise surprise - back to our familiar friend, the old 'freezing in the gutter' scenario. The reason that so many liars get away with so much for so long in their close relationships is that the other person fears for the changes that may be required in their domestic situation if the deception was to be exposed, therefore setting off the whole familiar chain of security/survival responses. Many liars are absolutely aware of this, therefore their deceptions remain unchallenged.

But who's the real victim in all of this? Is there a victim? Or do both characters in this story have a part to play in this desperately destructive dynamic. *Unravelling* <u>hates</u> people being ruled by insecurity. Not from any sort of opinion that it may hold about such things, but because insecurity is in itself a LIE. The truth is that the Universe and our life within it is inherently safe. We are born, and we die, and in between we are provided for to some degree or other. This statement, I believe, is inarguable. Every second of the time that we spend alive, is down to the fact that we are provided for. So there is no need to fear change (as long as, that is, we have no fear of our eventual and inevitable demise). We could argue that we want our lives to last for as long as is humanly possible, and that inviting change through exposing the lies of our close ones may be dangerous to our well-being and thus works contrary to this longevity project. It is this line of reasoning that results in so many settling for so much less than they really deserve, and by virtue of this, developing so much less of their potential than is their birthright.

So, because insecurity is not a 'true' thing - not aligned to the trueness of the actual safety of life in this Universe, and <u>definitely</u> not aligned to realising ourselves as being living expressions of this truth - *Unravelling* <u>will</u> root out this lie and offer to the insecure person their freedom. How is this done? With more lies! Unless the liar continues to lie there is absolutely zero chance of the insecurity being exposed as a sham! So the liar in a relationship cannot 'change their ways' for as long as the 'insecure' member of the dynamic, (the 'victim') is unable to own up to <u>their</u> lie, which is their 'fear' of losing their 'security'. (Sorry for all the inverted commas but hope you can see why I'm bracketing the words that seem to have developed such accepted and fixed meanings in the general parlance around relationship issues.)

So the liar keeps lying, and the infidelities/deceptions get worse. They have to, otherwise neither person will ever be granted their freedom. Eventually the level of deception is big and complicated enough to be exposed, and the whole edifice comes tumbling down. Then what happens? Sometimes, both parties move on. The 'insecure' one is then given a chance through a period of solitude to disprove the myth that they have erected that domestic change will result in their annihilation. The 'deceptive' one will be forced to sit for a while and consider the consequences of their deception.

If a new relationship comes along, there will be a fresh opportunity to demonstrate a little more faith in the security that is innate within an honest human life. On the other hand, this may happen...

*"Don't worry darling. I forgive you. Let's give it another try."*

Now they're really in the s\*\*t. Unless the 'insecure' one starts to develop some faith, the liar will and <u>must</u> continue with their deception. *Unravelling* will not cease its insistent intervention into this state of affairs until both parties have found honesty within themselves. So if the insecure one 'forgives' the deceptive one, there is a real chance of a semiconscious collusion that will accompany both parties to their graves and pass on untold levels of misery to future generations of their family.

Who's the victim in this sorry little tale? Classically, the deceived one gets the sympathy vote, but as lies go, theirs is a <u>real</u> whopper. Their real crime? To shut down on their sensitivity, thus overriding and ignoring the messages that are coming to them day after day, informing them that they are being lied to. We often give the scared or insecure person the benefit of the doubt in these situations, but this is a case of <u>wilful</u> ignorance, and needs to be called to account just as much as the more obvious act of deception by the 'liar'.

As we have seen, withholding in any form has a hugely detrimental effect on the withholder, and this shutting down on sensitivity is yet another form of withholding. The information that alerts a person to an incoming lie is sensed by their internal radar, the body transmits the information and flags it up to their awareness in just the same way as they may be alerted to the need to eat or sleep, and then..... it gets ignored. Of course, anything that gets ignored <u>will</u> shout ever more loudly over time. The messages will be getting through on some level, but will be more or less unconsciously sidelined. This is another situation where the person may eventually develop a 'split' personality, with two different versions of reality attempting to jostle for position within their mind. When Bob, who has been deceived for many years finally succumbs to a breakdown, people mutter knowingly...

*"Everyone apart from Bob saw that one coming. He should never have married her. Ali always was a deceitful cow. He's better off without her. Poor old Bob."*

Strangely enough, you never hear anyone say:

"How dishonest of Bob. He convinced himself and everyone else for years and years that this life was unsafe, and due to his illusion of insecurity do you know what he did? He forced Ali into the position where she had affairs, gambled with their money, and eventually ended up in prison for bigamy! All because Bob wouldn't have a little faith in the ultimate safety of leading a human life in this amazingly benevolent Universe. Poor Ali!"

(Actually, reading that, I can see why no-one would say that. Anyone who spoke like that would probably be exiled to another planet...)

I suppose you could argue it either way, but either way, the second way of looking at the situation is far less common, although equally valid. The point here is that it does take two to tango, and the stance of the 'victim' is equally as dishonest as that of the 'aggressor'.

So, as we can see, withholding in any form has its consequences, and is at the root of much that we put into the category of 'human suffering'.

Here's another version...

# Unspoken Truths

Welcome to *Unspoken Truths Quiz!!*

Our volunteer, Lyra, thought that she had agreed to be filmed going about her business in the office last Tuesday afternoon as part of a documentary about shredders. What she <u>didn't</u> know is that we also bugged the phone call she made to her husband at 15.25, and - best of all - planted a hidden microphone inside her head! Those naughty *Unspoken Truths Quiz!!* people are at it again! (but we can tell from the viewing figures that secretly, you just *love* the show, so here we go).

Here's some of the fibs that we recorded issuing forth from Lyra's mouth as the afternoon progressed.

| | |
|---|---|
| 1 | *"What a lovely colour."* |
| 2 | *"Of course I love you dear."* |
| 3 | *"JonPaul's very creative isn't he..."* |
| 4 | *"I'm fine thank you."* |
| 5 | *"Pass the paperclips."* |

All you have to do is match them up with the corresponding *Unspoken Truth* which she retained in her cranium...

| | |
|---|---|
| A | *"I don't love you any more."* |
| B | *"That shirt is just awful."* |
| C | *"My God Frank, I don't half fancy you!"* |
| D | *"My life is a complete pile of sh\*\*e and I'm very close to calling it a day - permanently."* |
| E | *"I really don't like your comb-over"* |

*(The answers are, of course 1B 2A 3E 4D and 5C )* Tee hee.

Unspoken truths and their accompanying white fibs seem much more fun and far less damaging than big old barefaced lies now don't they? But hang on a minute. They are still based upon withholding and will involve a disturbance in the breathing to an extent. Let's rate these Unspoken Truths in order of their potential for damaging consequences.

The shirt thing (B) is probably the least problematic. He ain't going to wear the shirt in bed or every day, and if he's just a colleague then you may never encounter him in bed anyway and your comment may be the kindest thing that you could do for him. The haircut issue (E) could be a bit more tricky if it was your spouse, as he will wear it in bed *and* every day. Unrequited love (C) is definitely bad for the heart but may inadvertently drive one to the dizzying heights of poetic creativity. Staying in a relationship when the love is gone but stating otherwise (A) is unwise, unfair, and not at all life-enhancing. Variations on (D) are extremely common and the danger here speaks for itself.

To say or not to say - where should one draw the line? Tricky. Some unspoken truths are simply opinions and it may be polite to keep one's counsel when witnessing a fashion *faux pas* committed by a less than close friend. Things get a little more serious when the 'unspeaking' of an internal truth comes down to an *inability to voice one's own needs*. Obviously, in groups and relationships, a degree of compromise is always part of the deal. My wife wants fish for dinner, I would like chicken.

*"Fish alright for dinner, Phil?"*

Yeah. That's cool.

So have I just caused myself some damage by not stating my needs? Well, it depends how attached I am to my wanting. My usual way of assessing whether or not I have overridden my needs in an detrimental way, is to clock if I'm still thinking about the chicken five minutes later. On a different day, I might argue the toss.

*"Fish alright for dinner, lover?"*

I'd quite like chicken tonight.

*"We've got both in the fridge. Good call. Chicken it is."*

In the past, it was a major habit of mine to override my internal needs. I would say I didn't want something when I did want it. I would say that I liked something when I didn't. I would say just about ANYTHING based on my perception of what I believed the other person might want me to say. Bad. This style led me to a belief that I was SO easygoing, when in reality I was positively brimming with unspoken desire and resentment. I came to the point that I could hardly choose between this and that because I was so out of practice! I am pleased to say that of late, things have turned around admirably.

> *"Fish alright for dinner, lover?"*

> I'd quite like chicken tonight.

> *"No problem. I'll leave you a frying pan out"*

O well. Life as practice eh? I've always thought that if you're still 'ere there's obviously more to do!

# Witnessing and the Power of Mutual Confession

My recent confession of all secrets, witnessed by the dear and trusted other, and my witnessing of those that she offered to my ears - this process came about because of love. Specifically because of falling in love. I have fallen in love before, and the love that I have fallen into always felt good. It felt good for a while, sometimes longer, sometimes shorter, and then the not so good feelings returned.

I have recently fallen in love with the dear and trusted other. Not with HER, but WITH her. I opened, we opened, and the love came pouring out, or pouring in - whatever. There was definitely a pouring going on, and it felt good. I felt loose and spacious, warm and open and free, enthused about life and all that it has to offer. And then, after a couple of months, a curious thing started to happen. I looked in her eyes and felt that I couldn't quite look - not quite - not fully and constantly - not like a short while back. It had felt so easy, and now it felt so scary.

In the first few months there was an opening, a sharing. You tell me yours, and I'll tell you mine. Likes and dislikes, music and films, philosophies, hopes and dreams. The past. The good bits and the bad bits, but not all of the bits. No, not all of the bits. Not the REALLY ugly bits.

I was being drawn by openness, by the power of *Unravelling*, working through and out of my open heart, to reveal all, to get clean, to be witnessed and accepted for all of that which I am and have been. Accepted by another, and more importantly, by *myself* in the face of another. The ugly bits. No I don't think so. Let's stop there. I'll close down just a little. I won't walk any further in that direction, toward her, toward the dear and trusted other - I can't trust that much. Don't ask me to look deeply into your eyes any more.

So my walking toward her is over. Our developing relationship is over. Our relationship is not over, but it's no longer developing. What do I do? Do I stay still? Stalemate? Feigning intimacy whilst standing at this line, afraid to take a step further? I divert. My inability to trust and walk forward toward her sends my feet and my mind sideways and in circles, into little whirlpools and vortices of dishonesty. I'm out of the flow. Up shit creek without a paddle as they say. Feels bad. If I'm not heading toward her any more, then I'm heading away. Can't walk away. Need to create a rejection. I'll get her to push me away.

I'll start to tell untruths. Hide things. Where I've been. How long I've been there. I've not been anywhere that she shouldn't know about. I couldn't even tell her that I'd been to the supermarket - that I'd been for petrol on the way home. THAT's why I was ten minutes late. My neck is getting stiff. I'm getting headaches. I'm holding my breath in her presence.

We're both pretty sharp. We both notice a lot. We're drawn to being in love, like in the beginning, all warm and free and open, but a veil is coming down. Please look me in the eyes.....

"Did you do that?"
No.
"Are you sure?"
Pause
"Phil, tell me...?"
Yes.

I look. I see her. Deep in our eyes I see me. And her. I feel that warm and spacious feeling.

Let's talk dear one. Let's not lose that connection. Let's willingly go where this river is taking us, and for the first time in our lives be honest - ALL of the time. Why not? Why not make honesty a CHOICE - just like choosing to paint the bathroom green or wearing that pair of shoes today - a simple choice toward the telling of the truth. It's no mystery what the truth actually is - it's just a case of being willing and awake enough to let my breath, my throat, my tongue and my lips produce the right shapes, even in the face of that familiar feeling - that seething cauldron of fear which lives in the pit of my stomach. The feeling that tries to convince me that if I don't withhold then I am in mortal danger.

So we did it. All of it. The ugly and the downright repulsive. From yesterday, from last year, from the farthest corners of our lives and minds. It was hard. We were exhausted. It seems to have transformed our existence.

# THREE

## More Aids
## to Unravelling

*"Don't be afraid that your life will end;
be afraid that it will never begin"*

Grace Hansen

There is inner work to be done, that much is certain. Having received therapy for many years, attended a zillion workshops promising enlightenment, and having learned a multitude of techniques for the attainment of happiness, we now find ourselves unceremoniously dumped back on our own doorstep, so to speak, our worst suspicions confirmed. Changing the world 'out there' in any direct way was never going to be easy, and now we know for sure that the task is impossible. Good news! At least we now only have one thing to sort out. Ourselves!

But for most people (and rightly so) the fruits of their internal labour are most desperately wanted and needed in the world 'out there' as it were - in the comings and goings of their everyday life. In the world of home and relationships, family and work. It is in these spheres that we most want to see the results of our 'self-development'. We yearn for better interactions with those close to us, and less stuff going wrong. We want to be treated with respect by those whom we encounter, and to find an effective avenue for our affection, enthusiasm and passion. We want, in effect, a good life.

As I said way back at the beginning, we can *never* know what life is going to throw up in front of us, but hopefully the inner journey that we have taken has brought us to a place where we can meet disaster and triumph with equanimity, retaining our equilibrium whilst being tossed around upon the ocean swell of our existence. The dubious ways in which we have acted up to this point, both toward ourselves, and with others, will continue to produce their consequences - maybe for many years - but although we my feel a little battle-weary, if we are resolute to stay relaxed and gently present to whatever comes along in life, and as long as we refuse one hundred per cent to blame the world any longer for our woes, then we will prevail. The stability deep within us will begin to elicit more appropriate responses to incoming events, and will allow us to assess our dealings accurately, and therefore make better decisions. Helpful people will be naturally attracted to our clarity, allowing for us a better sense of and purpose and engagement with our community.

At this point, the baseline of our well-being is on the ascendant, and now there's no stopping it. Once enough momentum has been gathered toward the new direction, it would take an awful lot of energy to slam on the brakes and go into reverse. We'd have to do some very stupid stuff for a considerable period of time to make the boat turn around now.

# LIFE

Many have asked the question..."What is the meaning of life?". But what is this actual *life* thing that I am so concerned with? When I say "my life" what exactly is it that I am referring to? My life is kind of 'out there' somewhere, and I only know anything about it because it is presented to me, and registered by me by way of incoming sensory perceptions, picked up by my awareness, and then validated as 'real' via the offering of my *attention* to those perceptions. Is there actually anything 'out there'...? How can I be sure?

I know that I am a-living because I <u>see</u> the stars, <u>hear</u> the birds or the voices of those who have passed over, <u>smell</u> the coffee, <u>taste</u> the cookie, and <u>feel</u> the warmth of the sun on my skin, the pangs of hunger in my belly. If I was having no sensory experience, how would I know if I were alive? Would I be alive? When someone returns from spending six months in a coma, we can tell them that they were indeed alive - we could see them lying in the hospital. But does not our seeing of them only go to prove that <u>we</u> are alive? When the person is in a coma, are they having sensory experiences? Or is it their *awareness* that has disappeared so that those experiences are not recalled? Maybe their *attention* has gone AWOL so that there is no effective link between their incoming sensory experience and their awareness.

More questions. When we die and thereafter, do we continue to have awareness of sensory material? Does the body drop away and our sensory faculties continue albeit in a different form? I have been told that this may be the case but I do not know for sure. Do those who have told me this 'fact' know? Have they been dead to find out? Who told *them* that this was so? Were they informed by ex-dead people who had returned to report on the afterlife? I was told by someone that they had experienced past lives. Had they? I know that they were describing to me some images and 'memories' that surrounded a narrative present in their mind at that moment, but I don't know for certain anything much more than that.

I'm a bit of a sceptic. I trust my senses because really and truly that's all I have to go on. If I have inner visions of angels then that will confirm my belief in inner visions, not in angels. If an angel stands before me and shakes me by the hand I may begin to entertain the possibility of angels 'out there' (given a few repeated experiences). If I hear a voice in my head, then so be it. Voice in my head, sound of the birds - just sounds coming in. If the voice tells me that I am invincible and should prove it by jumping headfirst from the Eiffel Tower, well I'm sorry but that's not going to happen. If I see colours around someone's head (which I did once without so much as a by your leave) then... how pretty. If someone tells me that this ability to 'perceive auric fields' means something and that I should change my life because of it then I'll tell them to leg it. If it starts happening every day then I'll be on the 'phone to them *toute de suite* to get some advice on the matter.

Our senses are wide and broad. We may have a sixth or sixtieth sense that opens itself for business as we develop and evolve as human beings. But whatever the nature or content of the information that's coming in, it's just information coming in. Impressions, in the form of pictures, sounds, smells, tastes and sensations within my body. Wherever it's coming from it all ends up in the same place as it is offered up to my awareness at the altar of the Impartial Observer. Not complicated. Simple.

The more interesting questions with regard to 'life' are these... what do I actually *do* with this information? How much of this incoming information has great meaning for me? Does it *all* have meaning? Does *any* of it have meaning? And the most significant question of all? What ACTION should I take on receipt of this information? Should I MOVE AWAY? Should I PULL TOWARD? Maybe I would be wise to FOLLOW? Or perhaps PUSH AWAY? From a meditative perspective I just register and do nothing. Mental image comes in... back to the breath. Sound comes in.... back to the breath. Smell comes in.... back to the breath - return to centre. This is a good practice. Keep returning to the centre. Don't get caught up. But is this approach suitable for day to day existence 'out there' in the big wide world? Surely human life is an action path - can't just sit around on a cushion for ever! When sensory information heads my way I cannot <u>not</u> respond. Perception will always stimulate within my system an attraction or repulsion with regard to the information contained within it, in either a subtle, or a more gross or knee-jerk reflex sort of way. How I then translate my perception into a choice of language and *actions* in the world is the more important issue, as it is these actions that will create *consequences* for me.

As we have seen, when we are *disorganised*, our use of the four emotional strategies will be highly habituated, and like any repetitive habit, will bring difficulty into our lives and an accumulation of tension into our bodies. This tension is always attempting to find release through the unwitting but appropriate creation of illness and personal crisis (another wave from the kindly hand of *Unravelling*). When we are centred, relaxed and in balance however, we naturally begin to develop the skill of *discernment* in relation to incoming information, manifesting an accuracy of response that allows us to retain connection with, and then return to, our centre. In balance, we can reach out from that neutral and 'ready' position, resulting in an effortless and sensitive exploration, utilising all of our investigative antennae. When someone is described as having a 'balanced view' or being 'balanced in their approach' we are talking about someone who is alert, but relaxed. Someone who has an open mind to new material but is not too easily swayed. Someone who is considered in the changes that they make to their beliefs about 'reality', and steady and progressive in their approach towards their choice of engagements in life. This person will be resolute but gentle. They may choose to modify their mindset or move their feet in a different direction, but never through coercion by another, or from a position of uncertainty.

If we were to talk to a random group of people about their ways of seeing the world, we would encounter a range of beliefs (a belief being defined as a viewpoint that has become fully convincing to that person). As we have already seen, our mindset as an individual is shaped by way of our habitual response strategy to incoming experience. Our response will in turn elicit a response from our environment which may then serve to reinforce our mindset.

Anyone who is highly habituated in their response strategies will be extremely convinced by their own opinions (their 'truth'). To protect this 'truth' they may choose to only keep company of others who support their view, and they may potentially come across as quite dogmatic or possibly evangelical. They may come to see 'their truth' as 'The Truth'. They will look at situations and selectively see only the information that reinforces their view. Any challenge to 'The Truth' may be met with hostility, dismissal, indifference, or anxiety. On the other side of the coin, they will be extremely easy to influence and manipulate by a leader who affirms their mindset. This polarisation of mindset is the genesis of 'cultish' behaviour. Those who are 'in' are OK, the 'rest' an enemy to be guarded against, or even destroyed.

How we respond as individuals, to incoming sensory information depends on how deeply we subscribe to one of the four so-called *philosophical extremes*. If I cite myself as an ETERNALIST, I hold the belief that everything that I experience holds meaning for me. For a NIHILIST, there's no meaning in anything. The MONIST believes that everything is one, whereas the DUALIST sees everything as being separate.

The NIHILIST is likely to PUSH AWAY incoming information. If there is no meaning in the information contained in the perception, then it will not be deemed worthy of

---

being delivered to their awareness. Why would it? There's nothing to be learned. So the channel shuts down. Use it or lose it. Eventually they may magnify this tendency and MOVE their attention AWAY from the information entering into their own sensory channels, diminishing the function of the sense organ itself. The unfortunate consequences for the nihilist are of a grey and meaningless existence and lack of communal experience.

The ETERNALIST however, will see great meaning even in the falling of a feather before their feet. Their sensory channels are wide open and searching. They will PULL TOWARD themselves more and more sensory experience. They may even find their perceptions becoming heightened, developing methods of picking up information beyond the scope of most. This may result in FOLLOWING, in the belief that everything that they see and hear contains personal meaning, and therefore they cannot afford to miss a thing! They may end up tormented by tiny everyday occurrences, believing that the presence of the feather is a 'sign' and demands subsequent action.

The MONIST finds it quite difficult to differentiate between 'things'. If everything is one, then there is no real need to move - no need to travel between here and there. The whole concept of time becomes lost on the monist, and they may end up quite directionless, uninterested in the material world, and more than a little rocklike. They may end up so inert that even sensory information does not notice their highly effective boulderish disguise and will pass them by. They have little need for a strategy. All has become still.

For the DUALIST, there is no peace. To experience the world they need to be in two places at once. Busyness and restlessness are their trademarks. They will be FOLLOWING and PULLING TOWARD closely followed by PUSHING AWAY and MOVING AWAY, all in quick succession. They are likely to be found either in a manic whirl or an exhausted heap.

Because each of these four philosophical stances are highly displaced to only one limb of a four-armed cross, they are generally unsustainable for the whole lifetime of a person. Anything in an extreme has a tendency to flip, often quite suddenly into its opposite position. For the 'balanced' individual, all of these views are valid, but none are subscribed to exclusively at the expense of the other three. To the centred person, everything does have meaning, but not everything has personal meaning. All is one - the whole universe is composed of the same stuff - but that 'stuff' takes on different forms that allow for an appropriate individuality of each object and being. By positioning ourselves gently at the centre of these four aspects of understanding, the mind will be alert, relaxed and ready to engage with that which it is called upon to deal with.

I feel that Descartes missed a trick and narrowed his options when he said...

"*I think therefore I am.*"

Personally, *I* know that I am by way of my <u>perceptions</u>.

**I SEE** an inner or an outer image therefore I know that I am alive.

**I HEAR** and I know that there is someone in here listening.

**I SMELL** so there is something to smell out there and also a smeller in here to do the smelling.

**I TASTE** and I know that the taster and the tasted are different.

**I FEEL SENSATION** in my body and I know where I live.

**I KNOW** myself by the difference between me and that.

**I AM THAT**, I AM (oh yes I am).

By way of perception, my life reveals itself.

# AIDS TO LIFE

## Space

Making space between things is the secret to good art. In visual presentations, it is often the 'white space' that singles out an attractive advertisement. It is the pauses in a musical piece that allow us to fill with appreciation for the mastery of the musician and the composer. When we listen to dazzling oratory, it is the space between sentences, where something 'hangs in the air' that offers us full appreciation of the experience.

Making spaces in our life is crucial. This is not simply an aesthetic or luxurious option. Spaciousness is a quality that is built in to the design blueprint of our anatomy and physiology. It is the space between bones that allows us the articulation of the joints of our skeleton, offering ambulation to our body. The space that exists between organs and structures within the body allows for a slooshiness that makes for good communication and flow of substances within the fluids. Between the beats of the heart is the resting space that holds the promise of the next beat, allowing our life to continue.

The space for replenishment and repair is offered to our body by way of the gift of sleep. We have an innate desire for tea and lunch breaks, siestas and Sundays, holidays and sabbaticals. All of these things have appeared in our culture because of the natural need for space amongst the 'things' of life. Spaciousness has had a bit of a bad press in many quarters of late. The culture of fullness - as much stuff as we can pack in - combined with a level of uneasiness around being perceived as 'lazy' has done much to diminish our appreciation of the necessity for spaciousness within our existence.

## Balance

Everywhere that we choose to look, we will find things existing in oppositional relationships.

Left and right, day and night,
Front and back, plenty and lack.

Inner and outer, faithful and doubter,
Straightness and bendings, startings and endings.

Up and down, (but not round and round),
Give and take, destroy and make.

Each single quality only exists in relation to its opposite, and the pairs exist to describe a greater whole. For example, we need a definite *something* for that something to actually exhibit a right and left aspect.

Some oppositional pairs are fairly fixed. To the observer, left will always be to that particular side of the centre, no matter how far away from the centre it might be. Day and night, however, are more variable. At certain times of the year, at a certain location on the globe there will be more nightdark than daylight. At the high point of the year it may seem as if light has completely overwhelmed the darkness, only to be reversed exactly six months later. These opposites are useful. They allow us to locate ourselves in space and time, and in relation to other people. If we tried to use only one side of an oppositional pair to describe our position, it would be nigh on impossible, as we would have no comparative reference point.

In the human system, as I have portrayed it throughout this book, one of our primary aims is to develop an awareness of our CENTRE. This centre is represented physically in the spinal column. The spine is the reference point around which the polarities of left and right, front and back, up and down play out their constant dance of interrelationship during the rhythmic acts of locomotion.

Emotionally, we have seen how the four simple strategies of orientation interweave their subtle directional messages toward the preservation and sustenance of our life. I have emphasised the importance of not getting stuck 'out on a limb' either though repetitive use of one side of the body, or through a habitual default style of emotional response. When our awareness is located at the CENTRE of a multi-polarity system such as the one that goes to make up our human being-ness, we are able to gently, safely, and accurately extend ourselves into the exploration of our inner and outer environment, and easily return to neutral. Working from the centre, the simple bare awareness of the Impartial Observer becomes as a fulcrum point of the see saw - there are forces playing out around us and within us, but all moves effortlessly around the still point. We become the empty "I" of the hurricane.

In life too, there are certain pairs of opposites that are worthy of our consideration and acknowledgement. Work and play. Activity and rest. Self and other. Logical and animal. Offering and receiving. Adult and child. Business and pleasure. A balanced life contains ALL of these qualities in equal measure, and because all of the qualities are acknowledged and lived out deliberately and consciously, and the centre is strong and stable, the balance that results is not a static affair, but will throughput a vast amount of dynamic energy. When we observe the spinning and play of an experienced ice skater, we are witnessing a remarkable expertise in acknowledgement and preservation of the central axis of the body. The greater their ability on this level, the higher is the level of power that can be delivered into the gymnastic performance.

When we are off-centre in our life's endeavour - maybe working too hard at the expense of playtime - our energy will be sapped by this one-sided approach. If play is absent, the world of work will become hard work. In the physical body, this correlates to carrying a heavy bag for miles and miles and years and years using only the right hand. The right hand will eventually tire and if we do nothing to bring the left side into play, then eventually the body will be unable to carry in either hand because of the effect that this one-sided activity will have on the supportive structures of our back. If both work and play are respectfully in place, then they each will benefit from the other's presence, allowing a passion and enthusiasm for both.

And what about the balance of head and body, of the upper and lower pole of our human playground? Our attention, as we have seen, goes wherever it is directed. We may spend most of our life living 'in our head' with our attention drawn toward the sensory organs that cluster closely around our skull, or be fascinated by the memories, conundrums and phantasmagorical imaginings that swirl around inside our craniums. This attention to mental dealings may well be a conscious choice. I may be a professor of astrophysics whose day to day demands that I take up permanent residence in the turret room library of *Castle Homo Sapiens*. On the other hand, it may not be a choice. My mental world may be so unstoppably busy that it sucks in every ounce of my attention like some pesky dust-devil. My choosing of the head-end as my place of residence may also represent an escape - an attempt to divert upwards from the grumbling uncertainty and animal growlings down below. Whichever it may be, the danger is that I may spend so much of my day up in headworld that I either forget to eat or to concentrate effectively on the road ahead, and inadvertently shuffle off this mortal coil.

Alternatively, the inner workings of my upper reaches may be a strange land to me. I may be more easily magnetised by my belly's yearnings and the cravings of my pelvic regions, forever scanning my environment for the next stimulating body hit.

Attempting to balance these two ends around the fulcrum of the human heart is a very fine endeavour indeed. By lodging our attention deliberately within the centre of our chest, we are in close proximity to both head *and* guts. The heart holds the supreme position within our human system. As mediator of top and bottom, it has the ear and confidence of both. It knows all that is worth knowing, and is a trustworthy guide. It was not without insight that the ancients of Chinese medical philosophy referred to the the vault of the cranium, rather demeaningly, as the 'muddy ball hall', and bestowed upon the heart the title of 'Emperor's palace'. By simultaneously acknowledging and giving expression to both the lofty aspirations of our mind, and also gently submitting to the instinct that thrives at our base, and then following our 'heart's desire' we come as close as we can be to the heart of *Unravelling's* simple message.

# Rhythm and Cycles

The polarity of activity and passivity is probably the most fundamental pairing of all. Go. Stop. Move. Be still. One of the fascinations of living at the latitude of the UK on the surface of a tilted planet which annually circumbobulates the sun, is that there is a constant shift of the proportions of light and darkness throughout the year. We can observe in nature how this light/dark balance has its cyclical effects on the growth, fruiting, decay and rejuvenation of plants and animals. Our relationship with the animal within our human can be much enhanced by tuning in to this revolutionary activity.

Within a single day, activity is most suited to daylight hours, the night time being the optimum place for our rest. Doing hard physical work in the morning and then switching to lighter tasks toward evening time is appropriate, as this approach ties in with the waxing and waning of the daylight. In the summer it is quite appropriate to exhibit a greater level of activity, and to be active for a greater proportion of the day, whereas in the winter, a leaning toward longer periods of resting time and more philosophical and reflective pursuits is eminently suitable. By matching our personal rhythms with those waveforms demonstrated unerringly within the natural environment, we are obliged to <u>notice</u> that which goes on around and above us, on the earth and in the sky. This can do us nothing but good. I highly recommend the practice.

In a whole lifetime, we will flourish admirably if we acknowledge the waxing and waning process. First half IS different to second half. Our body DOES change as the years progress. In acknowledging these changes, we can adjust the PACE that we choose to operate within our life as each year the Sun returns in its round to its starting point. Each year-end invites a review. Should I do things the same this coming year? Or differently? My eighty-five year old trekker had it nailed. For each decade that passed when she was over the age of fifty she deliberately dropped her pace by eight per cent. Nice. Spookily precise - but nice.

# Change

Everything comes, and everything goes. If things come, they will go - things that arrive don't stay. Even on arriving, they turn to go again, even if just a fraction. When they are obviously here, they are preparing to leave. When they are here most fully, they have already started to move away. On receding, they may return again at another time, albeit in a different form, but maybe as something very similar.

The above is true for spring, summer, autumn, winter, day, night, youth, success, despair, success, infamy, life, death, interest rates. One thing is never one thing because it is always heading toward the thing that it isn't, even when it is still heading into the thing that it is yet to become more fully. As it swings toward the right, the inevitable swing toward the left is positively swelling in its potentiality.

This is why worrying is (really and truly) a bit of a silly waste of time. Change is the only certainty, and confidence in this certainty is our greatest friend in times of despair and hopelessness. It's worth bringing the reliable truth of constant change to our awareness. What better way is there to do this, than to fall in love with the seasons. How I would greatly dislike living in a country with a consistent climate. In what manner would I be reminded so starkly of the truth of constant change?

Looking for certainty and stability is an occupation fraught with great dangers. It tries to make things and situations out of stuff of which they are *definitely* not suited. Every attempt to create a still point of understanding, time or relationship is thwarted by the very movement of its location through space. We are on a moving planet in a moving solar system in a moving galaxy for heaven's sake!

Letting go of certainty, releasing the need for a particular outcome to a situation, and embracing the Great Whatever, is a sure-fire recipe for relaxation.

# Wisdom and Growth

I believe that the greatest wisdom of all, is that of giving one's self the permission to 'not know'. The opposite of this, 'knowing' has a sort of finality to it, and suggests a wilful closure of the gateway to further learning, - a diminishment of curiosity. A closing down.

*"I KNOW (therefore there is no real reason to either look or listen)."*

In choosing the path of 'not knowing', my curiosity becomes childlike - all bright-eyed and bushy tailed. I'll be constantly on the lookout: thirsty for opportunities to evolve, and improve upon my current state of being. When 'I know', then I am clearly stating that I am satisfied with my current state of being, but more than that, it is an indication of a desire and willingness to *defend* my current state of being against further change and growth. Why would I be so keen to maintain this status quo?

Let's say that the area within Circle A below represents all of the 'stuff' that I know on this day, 2nd August 2009. A few years hence I will probably know more stuff, and so this could be represented by the contents of larger Circle B.

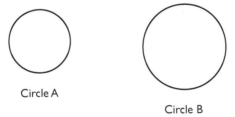

Circle A

Circle B

If I am generally someone who says 'I know', then the transition from A to B may be uncomfortable. The inside of the circle also represents my comfort zone, and the stretching and widening of the circle to accommodate new material may be a little painful as I come up against the resistant 'growing edge' of my knowledge in my encounter with 'the unknown'. If I am the kind of person who is prepared to cultivate the practice of 'not knowing' as a way of being, there is a good chance that circle A has a far more elastic quality to it - making the inclusion and ingestion of new material a far more comfortable experience.

To 'not know' takes a certain amount of courage in the face of encountering new territory. What may there be outside of my Circle A? Will it be dangerous? In olden times, the village was bounded by watch towers, and fires at night to repel intruders and keep out the wild animals that may have come in to pilfer the odd sheep. Occasionally, a foolhardy villager would stray past the boundaries, never to be seen again. And then one day, one of these long-lost 'crazies' would turn up to the amazement of the villagers, with miraculous stories of far distant lands and peoples, bringing with them strange songs and sporting outlandish fashions.

To go beyond the circle may be hazardous. Some may be lost to the wilderness, but the culture of both the village, and the mindset of the an individual must change and grow. Every system is subject to the evolutionary might of the force of *Unravelling*, which is beyond the control of any being. To raise a flag for stasis is to usher forth the brittling process that eventually takes the body and mind towards inflexibility, stagnation and a premature death.

Any potential learning that I receive comes to me initially as information via my senses. For my mental process to create *meaning* from this information, I need to offer my *attention* to the sensory input in a reasonably undivided way. I will then have the opportunity to *register* and *absorb* the incoming data, and I can then compare and contrast previously inputted information, (accessed from memory) to the new stuff, and make informed choices about the possibility of reshaping the current nature of my 'mindset.' My mindset, combined with my tendency to conditioned and distorted emotional response strategies, is the basis for my actions in the world. The informational feedback that I then receive from the world in relation to my actions (good results or not so good results) allows me to 'learn from my experience'.

I used to think that 'learning from experience' was the way that wisdom developed, but if I insist on 'knowing' (as outlined above) I'll probably disbelieve negative feedback that comes back to me from the world and keep on going with the same old strategy, believing it to be 'right' simply because 'I know'. If I change my tack and entertain the possibility of 'not knowing' then my awakened curiosity will allow me to glean far more from the incoming feedback and see greater possibilities for evolving my mindset, and for creating more constructive and creative patterns of behaviour.

I deduce from this that wisdom, in the conventional sense, does <u>not</u> arise from learning and experience, but that it is the ultimate wisdom of 'not knowing' that is a prerequisite to learning anything. 'Not knowing' - an open and curious inquisition toward our experience of life - is the most effective lubricant of natural growth.

# Navigating Challenge

If we choose to walk the path of 'not knowing' then our system remains soft, and curious toward incoming information and events. Within that softness is a sensitivity that allows an accurate appraisal of changing circumstance. This will result in an appropriate response to alterations in our environment.

We only have two options in the face of change. We will either stiffen or soften. Stiffening, which will result in a general clenching within the musculature of our body, decreases our sensitivity, and therefore diminishes our ability to know with accuracy what to do next. Softening, or YIELDING to change and challenges (which are usually changes) allows us to accurately LISTEN, and to SENSE via our internal radar system, the nature of the incoming stimulus.

Having listened accurately, we can then allow our body to decide whether it wishes to MOVE AWAY, FOLLOW, PUSH AWAY or PULL TOWARD in relation to the stimulus. If the energy of the stimulus threatens to move us off our carefully cultivated centre, we can choose to take a step back to gather ourselves, or turn ourselves to DIVERT the energy of the incoming force of change so that it passes us by. To habitually meet the energy of problems head-on is probably the least useful strategy that we can take. This strategy breeds a tendency to stiffen as we sense the approaching challenge, hoping to God that the force that's coming in isn't heavier than us! This way of being will over time produce a general level of armouring of the musculature within our body, as we brace ourselves in preparation for even the smallest incoming alteration in circumstance.

If we allow ourselves to yield and divert the incoming force slightly, we have an opportunity to 'get a handle' on the situation, view it from a slightly different angle, and to use the energy that's contained within the approaching change to our advantage. In this way, we gain a certain level of control over the situation. If we have been successful in the sequence of sensing, yielding, diverting and controlling, thereby preserving our own centre and preventing ourselves from being knocked off our perch, it is then - and only then - that we should act. In this way, our actions will come from a stable place. We have both feet rooted to the floor, an acknowledgement of our centre around which to manoeuvre, and a lightness of limb that allows us to apply a degree of gentle and fine manipulation to the situation at hand.

If we maintain this level of relaxed alertness within our body at all times when we are vertically active, then we will be literally, ready for anything. Because our mental, emotional and physical system is organised, even major changes and shocks will be met with the greatest of ease and problems despatched with consummate skill.

# Wonder

There is something bigger. There is always something bigger. Bigger than me, bigger than us, bigger than this issue, that crisis, this life, this earth, this solar system.

The bigness of things leaves me silent. My own mortal frame, my own life, my own chatter, for a while diminished by the awesome bigness of it all.

I remember lying on my back in my Aunt Jessie's garden, amongst the blackcurrant bushes, finding a gap in the foliage where I could see the vivid blue of the sky and the passing of brightest boiling white cumulus clouds. I don't know where I went. I don't know where the time went. I disappeared.

I remember lying on my back on the lawn at my parent's house. On a blanket, in a blanket. Freezing winter evening. No blue, no clouds. Icy pinpricks of the stars blazing back at me. I remember not looking at the stars, but looking at the space in between, imagining it as distance, not just a black canvas. That the stars were in front of and behind each other. That there were stars on the other side of the Earth on which I lay, behind me - stars *behind* me. For the odd moment I felt me, the Earth, all of us and all that I knew, suspended in and by nothing. Just for a moment. I disappear.

> "Phil.... come inside! You'll catch your death!"

Or possibly glimpse my life...
I'm back.

I remember on the Dorset coast, one evening in August 1979. A massive electrical storm. I was out in it. Me out in *it*. Me and it out together. It and me just out there on the headland. Me not smaller any more but bigger, with the storm. It and me together. I disappear.

I remember the Moon - first time through binoculars. Oh my God! It's made of rock. The edges of craters and dark moon sunset horizon. Crisp definition. Oh my God! It's real - it's really just hanging there in space. I disappear.

I remember the Sun. Deep red, disappearing below the scratched industrial horizon of my childhood playground. Big. Getting Bigger. Even Bigger. Where is it? Balanced on the end of my finger? On the horizon? Or as far away as they say in the books? Going. Going. Gone. I disappear again.

I remember the snow. One crystal on the window pane. A whole city of turrets and spikes in one flake. A whole world. Cold out there. Warm in here. The cold out there heated by the warm in here. The city vanishes to a droplet in an instant. A whole city vanished. Warm in here cooled by cold out there? I disappear.

Who am I that I can disappear and reappear with such regularity and ease? Did I disappear? I don't know. I wasn't there to see. I went out there. Out there came in here. *Someone* was there. There was an unmistakable feeling of wonder that was being experienced by someone. Or maybe that wonder was in the nature of the sky, the clouds, the stars, the moon, the thunder and the sun, the snowflake, the me. It just made friends with itself, and I disappeared.

It felt.... simply wonderful.

Always make time to look up. Take time to lie down. Make time to look *way* out there. It may take time to feel *way* in here. Ask the simple questions. See the answers coming right back at you. Feel the something vast in the something tiny. Make time to disappear and see what remains. Be filled with wonder, and be wonderful.

If you're not there, *Unravelling* still will be. It'll be looking out for you. Let it catch you.

# Faith

*Is it safe?*

Is what safe?

*"Just going with it."*

Of course it's safe.

*How do I know it's safe?*

You don't know it's safe. You give it a go. Then you'll know if it's safe or not.

*But what if I give it a go and find that it isn't safe?*

Say more?

*I might "just go with it"- y'know... let go - and I might die.*

You'll die anyway at some point.

*But I don't want to die early!*

You may die today. A satellite might fall out of the sky and land on your house. How would you know if you'd died "early"? Give it a go. You've got nothing to lose but the tension that you've been using to 'hold on' for all these years.

*Oh...*
*But if I let go, and "just go with" it, will I suffer? Will it hurt?*

It may do, but only for a while. Anyhow, you're suffering already. Would we be having this conversation if you weren't hurting somewhere?

*S'pose not.... So is it safe?*

Yes.

*How d'you know?*

I tried it. The sky didn't fall in.

*But what if I let go, "just go with it" and my life changes - all that I have built changes.... falls apart.*

Everything you have now has your 'holding on' tension built into its foundations. If it goes, everything gets built again from the ground floor upwards, but with much more ease at its roots. Besides, 'all that you have built' may not go. It may just change shape a bit; become a little easier to work with.

*I obviously have no faith.*

Don't worry about faith. Go for experience. In the light of experience, faith becomes irrelevant. Faith with no experience is just theory developed from someone else's experience.

*But I need to know!*

Allow yourself the luxury of <u>not</u> knowing. If someone else's theory <u>feels</u> right, then try it for size. Then you'll know.

*But what if I should die!*

Then you'll never get the chance to know how foolish you had been.

*Thanks.*

You're very welcome.

Dum-de-dum de-dum.
(Sigh)
Wanna buy a book....?

# Truth-telling

He said that telling the truth will set you free. It will. It will set you free because telling the truth makes you *feel* free, and allows you to breathe naturally. The living of a life free of secrets, a life where we have made a conscious decision toward the telling of the truth (however unpalatable), and where our individual needs are clearly spoken to ourselves and others, means that we can say so long and bid farewell to withholding in all of its many guises. The demise of withholding within our lives allows the breath to return to its natural shape, releasing the body and clearing the mind, leaving the slate blank for today to be just as it is, with all of its joys and challenges. With a free and natural breath, a relaxed and spacious body, and a mind uncluttered with all of the plate-spinning activity that is an inevitable accompaniment to an untruthful life, we will perceive with razor-sharp accuracy, respond appropriately, and act with absolute commitment.

In **telling** the truth, I can be bold, with the full energy of my being behind my words.

In **living** the truth, I can step through my world lightly, and with confidence, creating nothing that I will have to come back to sort out later.

In **being** the truth I can look deeply and constantly into the eyes of the dear and trusted other, and maybe into the eyes of others in my world, without fear, offering that way of looking as a possibility to them, and to those in their world.

The issue of 'truth' that I may once have considered to be an issue of morality, becomes then transformed into a matter of 'trueness' - the kind of trueness that we see in the flight of an arrow, let loose from the bow of the Master Archer, and striking effortlessly toward the bullseye - every time. The Master Archer would state with humility that he is still a student of his Art, the final five percent of his skill demanding the whole of the rest of his life to perfect. So with the Art of Truth-Telling. It is a *practice*, but fortunately there are a million and one opportunities every single day of our lives to refine our abilities. And every day we may fail. The real skill is in allowing ourselves to fall - and then resolving to get up and have another go.

I was once taught that being good and refraining from doing bad things would be the bringer of my salvation. Happiness, in actual fact, arises from telling the truth. In a truthful life, 'bad' actions do not arise - they cannot, as those bad actions are merely symptoms of a disconnection from one's own freedom - desperate cries for help from a closed heart. In the light of truth-telling, the impetus toward committing bad acts dissolves. Bad acts are not in accordance with the True Alignment that emerges from letting go into that unswerving river of Trueness - the great vector of the force of *Unravelling*. In the light of truth-telling, all re-laxes. All moves closer toward wellness.

For myself, I could not have made my confessions to another before now. I didn't have enough trust within me to make that leap. For that I am truly regretful, as I survey the human collateral - the broken hearts and damaged minds that lie strewn in my wake. Furthermore, it is only recently that I have taken delivery of the non-judgemental ears to listen to, and to hear the secrets uttered in whispered tones to me by her. The dear and trusted other appeared to me because we were *both* ready. I was tired of living my life in a closed-hearted manner. I wanted so much and for so long to meet her eyes and keep on looking. I got my wish fulfilled eventually. I am so very grateful.

Practising a truthful life within the confines of a primary relationship is a very good place to start. To take that openness into the larger arena of family members, friends, colleagues, neighbours and complete strangers is an ongoing practice, and should be handled with care. The mutual sharing of one's inner world with the dear and trusted other will produce a solid foundation for such a practice. To live an open-hearted life within the wider world demands a relaxed body, sharp perceptions, a clear mind and accuracy in emotional response. These things are, paradoxically, the product of the easy breathing that comes along with the practice of truth-telling. So one has to start somewhere.

We may wish to start this journey by telling *ourselves* our secrets and unspoken truths. We may have been lying to *ourselves* by convincing ourselves that certain elements either from our history or current experience 'don't really matter' - that we would be better leaving the lying to the sleeping dogs. Writing a *Letter To Self*, may be a good starting point to bring some awareness to the amount of charge that surrounds certain issues.

Working with a professional 'listener' may be a good next step. To hear ourselves stating to another attentive being that we are unhappy with certain aspects of our personal history, or with our current situation, and maybe with the behaviour of the characters who populate those dramas, can be a life-altering process. If we follow the recommendation of a personal friend toward a counsellor, we can be reasonably confident that this person will have the compassion, skill, and non-judgmental ear necessary to allow us to begin unpacking our luggage.

But it is the MUTUAL sharing that has the real power for redemption. To know that there is one one other human being on the planet that knows all of you, as you know all of them - that is where the liberation begins.

We do of course need to get the practice of truth-telling in some sort of context. *Of course* it's alright that I don't tell my dear one that I've planned a trip to Barbados for her birthday. It might cause me to hold my breath a little and for a little while - but only with excitement when I think of her opening the envelope with the tickets inside! *Of course* I may need to process an unspoken truth for a short period of time by myself without sharing - spend a little time wrangling over some internal problem before I make a decision to discuss it with someone else. And *of course* I'm not going to approach a complete stranger in the street and unload on to them a closet-load of skeletons! And remember, in the final analysis, the <u>content</u> is NOT the issue. Letting go of the contents of our closets is simply moving us TOWARD a practicable skill - the ability to make truth-telling a constant aspiration and a conscious moment-by-moment practice.

I also keep reminding myself that it's important to take a moment for reflection, before choosing to send a salvo of MY TRUTH toward an unsuspecting traffic warden. The practice of truth-telling should not be misconstrued as a licence to throw our OPINIONS around the place willy nilly.

I believe, given a little time, a keen eye, and a following wind, that there is a dear and trusted other for every-one. I also believe that the dear and trusted others are looking for each other, and that the chaos that ensues within our lives that seemingly tears our relationships and life situations asunder, only to start over again, are always opportunities for a truer state of being. The force of *Unravelling*, the great bringer of truth is knocking on the door of our hearts constantly - from the inside. Take time to listen to your heartbeat in the quiet deep of the night. Let it move you.

### EXERCISE SEVEN - TELLING THE TRUTH
Try this

Select a day - any day - and promise yourself that you are going to be completely truthful for the whole day. When you are asked something by somebody, do not lie. See what happens. If you wish to withhold information when asked asked a question by another, tell them that this is what you are doing. Don't fudge it.

# Living in Truth, Going Beyond Fear

I have been very careful during the writing of this part of the book to avoid positing the telling of truth or otherwise as a moral issue. I have deliberately diverted around, and tried to go beyond any discussion of the moral rightness or wrongness of keeping secrets, telling lies, or withholding truths from another. My aim has been to point out unequivocally that an untruthful life has far-reaching consequences - nothing more - and centrally that the consequences of withholding will reveal themselves without error, and immediately, via a detrimental change to the structure of our body due to an alteration in our breathing. The effects on our health, our happiness as individuals,

---

upon the others who share our lives, and on the society and the world in which we live, arrive later - but not that much later.

I have come to believe over the years, that 'making a positive difference' in the world boils down to my becoming aware of the quality of my **own** actions on the stage of life - how **I** am within the simple arena of my day to day living - **_that_** is the thing that will make a difference to my environment and for those with whom I share it. I believe that this inner work is my most effective way of being political, in a world where 'politics' as a force for positive change seems to have become an ever more ineffectual and disappointing arena. In addition, if things aren't working out for **me**, then I would do well to look toward my own internal machinations for answers, rather than attempting to change others in order to shape the world as I would like to see it.

The content of this book has pointed toward the promotion of _organisation_ as a way of improving and optimising good health - toward self-awareness, and practices of the body and its breath, alignment and relaxation as simple tools to employ on the path toward True Alignment. I feel that the the journey to trueness - and in particular toward telling the truth, and living a life based on truth-telling - away from withholding - is encouraged by these practices. But we also need to approach our goal by way of rock-solid intent. By creating within our heart and mind a resolve toward truth-telling, and by allowing that resolve to reveal itself within our lives via our voice. In this way, we actively re-create our body and our life daily, in a way which is pleasing and productive to ourselves, and in harmony with those who share our world. The beauty of this simple approach is that we can practise this intent in _every single interaction_ that we experience in our day. We KNOW whether or not we're telling the truth - it's not complicated. Allowing it to flow from our mouth has to become a matter of choice in each moment. As I said before: at any point in our lives we are either getting weller or we are becoming iller. Let's get the base line of our wellness heading upwards. It costs absolutely nothing and is something that we can strive toward during every minute of every day.

Remember sitting on that bench in the shopping centre? Watching all of those forward and backward-leaning people walk by, and then occasionally seeing that one in a hundred who's been lucky enough to retain their natural verticality? Remember how your heart leapt when you witnessed their effortless passage from stage left to stage right? Well, I hope that all of us at some stage in our lives have the great good fortune to come across that one in a million who has been blessed with a whole life of truthfulness. These people are obviously sent as Agents of *Unravelling*. We could call them saints. Because they have never held a secret, and have never allowed anything other than the truth to pass their lips, they break our hearts wide open when we look in their eyes, as we grieve for our own life part wasted. Having never created a convolution in their life's story, they never have cause to examine the past with regret. Being deeply rooted in attention to the present, they have gone beyond any fear of future events. They radiate the ultimate courage that arises from living in truth - that basic uncluttered presence that resides within each of us, which is waiting to be liberated as we surrender into True Alignment.

# Surrender

Life's a funny old thing ain't it? You get born - stuff happens - and then you die. Funny that.

Our perception of time as an arrow into the future sort of suggests that we're *going* somewhere. How ironic is it then, that the thing we're travelling *toward* is the end of our lives. And this particular end isn't like coming to the end of a long and arduous trip to be welcomed by a big log fire, a nice cup of tea and a pair of comfy slippers. No. This is THE end.

I have been told at various points during my life by those who claim to know, of alternative possibilities to my conclusion regarding the Big Conclusion, but my gut feeling is to reserve judgement until The Day Of said Judgement, (thanks all the same).

Those alternatives? Well, I have been reliably informed on the one hand that...

   a) If I was really good then all would be well
   (I think that this refers to a God-who-shall be obeyed)

and also...
   b) If I couldn't stop myself being really bad then everything would still be OK
   ('Glass half-full', Merciful and Kindly Bearded Uncle type of God)

alongside...

    c) If I was really bad then I would definitely end up in a VERY bad place
    (Wrathful and Scary Punishing God with more neatly trimmed
    Mephistophelian stylie beard)

and finally...

    d) If I was as good as I could *possibly* be then I'd still end up in a really bad place
    because I was in fact a nasty irredeemable little toad... (Glass Half-Empty
    and bitter sort of God)

So really, there was nowhere to go, and so in the light of this I have subscribed to **Endology** as a way of life. The Endological manifesto says that when you're done you're done - and that's it. (Incidentally, I used to be a fully paid-up member of the Reincarnation Society, but I eventually was asked to leave, simply because I was spending so much time focussing on the ins and outs of past and future lives that my lack of attention toward such simple things as driving a car was putting myself and others in considerable danger.)

One would have thought then, that as an Endologist, my life has become a helter-skelter of reckless abandon and the wildest of excess, leaving me a burnt-out husk with a trail of destruction in my wake, but actually I'm a bit of a moderate soul and really rather gentle and happy in my demeanour. I've done a few silly things but I'm really trying hard to sweep up after myself these days.

On the other hand, you may conclude that in taking Endology as my creed, my way of *re-ligaring* the threads of my life, that I would have become hopelessly depressed and morbid, with no zest for life, *joie de vivre*, or woohoo about me. On the contrary, I feel very committed and enthused towards my hopes and dreams, and feel able to be extremely attentive to those things that come to meet me along the way.

The conclusion I've come to is this. If THE END is what it says it is (that's THE END by the way), and if it does what it says on the tin, then I can leave it be. It's THE END, and that, as the Endologists say, is that. The future then, instead of masquerading as the 'great scary unknown' becomes an absolute dead cert - it's THE END - no worries. If my Endological philosophy is a heap of hogwash, however, then no worries either! I'll keep an open mind and deal with the great beardy one when he's ready to call me in.

Either way, Endology practice keeps me *fully attentive* to the ever-unfolding panorama of my life as it is offered to me in the present moment, whether that be the stuff in my inner world, or happenings in the place 'out there' beyond my skin. Endology has certainly stopped me from taking the ends off my fingernails whilst chopping vegetables and allows me to drive my car like a loony with FAR greater presence... but more importantly, it has quieted my mind of fearful future-fantasy and made peaceful a belly that used to seethe with dread.

## Surrendering the Will...
## ...and Taking the Reins Once More

Much of this book has been concerned with 'letting go'. I have implored you to 'not know' and 'just go with it'. Suggested that you allow, accept and surrender. I have asked of you that you may develop a little faith in the possibility of a benign and kindly force that reaches out from and into each one of us: a force that, if embraced rather than resisted, will bring about an appropriate level of order and improved health in our wearied and disorganised human system.

My suggestion to you of attempting the cultivation of these sorts of qualities may come across as a peculiarly passive way of dealing with life's difficulties (although as we have seen, the journey will demand the marshalling of a huge degree of self-awareness, which in itself may be the most mammoth task that we have ever set for ourselves). But these seemingly submissive acts are only the starting point - a preparation for a much more conscious way of living. In making the journey, we have undergone a thorough spring clean prior to our reaping some of the rewards that wait for us at the end of this arduous journey of self-discovery.

In the letting go - in the 'going with it', we allow *Unravelling* to clean us out. By aligning ourselves to gravity, and vertically resting in our bones, we allow a re-laxation which will detoxify our human system - body <u>and</u> mind - and allow the best chance of forgiveness; a 'clean slate' so to speak. The obvious benefits offered by a deeper level of emotional intelligence, combined with an intent toward truth-telling as our default, mean that our interactions with people, places and situations will become imbued with ever-increasing clarity and ease. Our mind, freed from the crazy monologue, offers us a little peace to accompany our comings and goings.

So what are we to do with this newly relaxed body? How should we employ this intelligent emotio-system of orientation, this peaceful mind, surrounded by its array of pin-sharp perceptive apparatus? What now? Sit round scratching our backsides contemplating the wonder of existence? I don't think so! After all, this human life is a *doing* sort of trip is it not? I can't for one moment believe that we were blessed with these wonderful endowments (which may, admittedly have become a bit messed up) and then had the good fortune and developed the necessary skills to have returned them to roadworthy condition, just so that we could lounge about for the rest of our lives eating nachos.

No. It's time to get on and feed something back into the system. We do now, after all, have some skills to teach. We have 'healed' ourselves. We may have had to go through the fires of *Halja* and high water to get there, but we have done it! We are now a more fully Human being than we have ever been. These refined qualities are the ones that a human being was always destined to exhibit, so let's get out there and show 'em what we're capable of.

You see, we can now <u>use</u> this human system. Up to now it's been demonically 'possessed' - our body filled with tension which we knew nothing about and therefore weren't able to release - our responses to other people unclear and unpredictable, creating a life where we were forever trying to sort out the collateral damage - and our mental space full of junk, which made even the planning of a shopping trip a nightmarish proposition! But now.... now I have a spanking shiny tool that works, and more to the point, one that is under some degree of control. Now then... what kind of a life should I craft with this brand new gizmo?

I'm obviously not planning a return to the clumsy oafish behaviour, the manipulative and weapon-like speech and the scheming and self-interested mindset that has been my default for ever and a day. I now notice myself acting in more appropriate and (for me at any rate) unusually effective ways. I seem to be able to find words that soothe rather than irritate, but which seem to be able to summon a commanding tone that is unfamiliar to me. My mind moves these days toward a 'bigger picture' whilst affirming a level of self-regard that I am unused to. At last I seem to be doing the 'right thing' more of the time. I seem to be drawn to act in ways that seem easy and effortless. Helpful circumstances and coincidences seem to rally, unbidden, to my side. I used to feel that my life was tainted - as if the Devil was sticking his foot out and tripping me up at every step, pushing me toward my own self-destruction. I'm not sure whose is the kindly hand that seems to guide me now. Perhaps the foot and the hand are both attached to the same mysterious friend. All of it may just be the invisible, omnipotent and tireless wisdom of *Unravelling* at work (that's my name for it - I'm sure you have your own). But I sure as hell am glad to have it as a friend by my side these days. It feels quite safe now to pick up the reins, attempt to keep my balance as I sit astride the awesome energy that it manifests through my body and in my life, and let it lead me along the route that it knows is absolutely the one that I am best suited for. It feels trustworthy. I'm very happy to surrender my will to the ride of a lifetime.

I have spent much of my life wondering why I am like I am, highly disgruntled by my crazy mind, wayward emotions and unpredictable body. I have looked to my history for answers and at times blamed others for my past and present state of suffering. In the belief that I was irredeemably flawed I have battled interminably with my urges and my behaviour, trying to fashion a more certain future. I have even looked further than the time span of this life for answers, and have found no certainty, my feelings about such things as past and future lives being at best, speculation, and at worst a huge distraction from this very moment.

And so, having gone full circle, and arriving with a bunch of memories and a few battle scars, here I am, just as I began - just me and my bottle of Tipp-Ex. Just sitting. Just noticing. Simply being - in the presence of my bodily sensations, my perceptions of light, sound, taste, smell, and those impressions that flood toward my awareness from the phantasmagoricum of my mind. I just am. No search. No result. No problem.

# AFTERWORD

## Being In Truth, Staying In Love

I am most pleasantly surprised that my recent excursion into confession, and the experience of being witnessed by the dear and trusted other has been followed by a huge 'change of heart' within me. I feel motivated toward staying truthful.

I like being in love. I'd like to stay in love. I realise now that two people cannot be in love unless they live in truth, and are prepared to tell each other the truth - all of the time, and for as long as they choose to share the intimate relationship space with each other. As soon as two people begin to deceive each other by way of secrets, lies or unspoken truths, they close the door to love and forfeit the access to each other's heart.

More tragically even than this, is the barrier that I create between my *own* heart and my *own* life when I choose to give up on honesty. The deep welling-up of the human heart is the source of uniqueness in a human life - 'following one's heart' (gently organised by the logic of the head of course) creates the opportunity for the authentic life that is our birthright and our duty. When my heart ceases to find a clear channel into my life, inspiration dries up, and conditioning takes over. I am deeply lessened by my drawing of a veil over my heart's urging.

In committing to the telling of truth, I align myself with the trueness of *Unravelling*. Having no thought for itself, *Unravelling* knows no way to provide anything other than reliable guidance. It pushes out centrifugally from the centre of every organised system - from every star, from the centre of our planet, the eye of every storm, the nucleus of every cell - and from the history and heart of every human. *Unravelling* is the ONE breath that breathes us all, and it looks to find its way into and through every resistance in every single form - whether galaxy, goldfish or human being - in an attempt to liberate every being that partakes in the glorious evolution of this remarkable Universe.

As we gently let go, with conscious awareness of a skilfully architectured body structure, into the gravitational field that the great teacher, *Unravelling*, provides on this blue and green Earth, we align ourselves with unswerving and unending provision. The soft and responsive body in which we reside comes into tone. The positions, flows and chambers become optimised. Our mind clears and our perceptions sharpen. We are ready. Ready to respond with consummate grace and skill to whatever might be heading our way. Like a string, awakened by the bow of time, we surrender ourselves to the universal symphony, within which the unique contribution of our individual, authentic and curious presence ever was indelibly scored.

Let the show begin.

# *Thanks and appreciation must surely go to...*

**...to my family** who made the container tight enough for me to feel safe, and loose enough for me to to walk my edges.

**...to my partners in crime this time** especially to my dear wife Joanne, who got me back to the animal(s) in the nick of time.

**...to my Teachers of movement** Roy Cliff, Rod Edlin, Balbinder Singh Dhaliwal, and to Raymond and Gavin Towers, who have changed my life more than they will probably ever realise.

**...to my Teachers of bodywork** John McTimoney, whom I never met, but whose towering presence stalks my every manoeuvre, and to Dr Fritz Smith, whose kind hands have gifted me, and this world, so so much.

Thanks also to all of those who have taken horizontal respite on my treatment table over the last seventeen years. Without you (as they say) none of this would have been possible.

And finally to Derek Bird. For unwittingly being in the place that he always hung out, at exactly the right moment.

# ACKNOWLEDGEMENTS

To Ashley at Able Design for the pagesetting and fabulous covers. Kevin Hyde for his martial friendship and for his remarkable BaGuaZhang postures. Linda Kempton, Dr Karen Cocksedge and Kev for looking over the manuscript and giving invaluable feedback. Joanne and Kev, and the escalator people of Westfield Derby for their sillhouettic contribution. And finally to Photoshop Elements 3.0 and my good old MacBook for holding it all together without a single crash!

I hope that you have enjoyed reading this book as much as I have enjoyed putting it together. It was quite a task, but now feels like quite an achievement. This book was self-published under the TrueAlignment banner. I find it a shame that authors, who put so much enthusiasm, life-time and energy into their projects, should receive so little financial reward for their efforts when they finally manage to get published by an established house. In self-publishing, this book I feel very happy that I receive an income which is more than pence per copy, and would wish that the proceeds contribute towards the ongoing development of my passion for projects that serve to promote TrueAlignment in this world. For this reason, if you have enjoyed the book, and would recommend it to a friend, don't lend it out... buy them their own copy as a birthday present!

I'd also be **really** grateful for any feedback that you would like to offer me about your experience of reading this book. So please... e-mail me!

and **Thank YOU** for reading ....

**UNRAVELLING - Letting Go, Getting Well.**

ON! ON! ON!

Further and more copies of this book can be obtained from the WebStore at:

**www.theUNRAVELLINGbook.com**

or alternatively, feel free to e-mail me with your order at:

**unravelling@btinternet.com**

For details of Phil's bodywork practice, and Zero Balancing teaching, go to:

**www.true-alignment.com**

For information on Zero Balancing, have a look at:

**www.zerobalancinguk.org**
**www.zerobalancing.com**